Stinging Fly Patrons

Many thanks to: Ann Barry, Maria Behan, Niamh Black, Denise Blake, Jane Blatchford, Celine Broughal, Trish Byrne, Edmond Condon, Evelyn Conlon, Sue Coyne, Liam Cusack, Michael J. Farrell, Kathy Gilfillan, Michael Gillen, Helene Gurian, Brendan Hackett, Nuala Jackson, Claire Keegan, Jerry Kelleher, Conor Kennedy, Gráinne Killeen, James Lawless, Joe Lawlor, Irene Rose Ledger, Wendy Lynch, Róisín McDermott, Petra McDonough, Lynn Mc Grane, Finbar McLoughlin, Maggie McLoughlin, Dan McMahon, Ama, Grace & Fraoch Mac Sweeney, Mary Mac Sweeney, Paddy & Moira McSweeney, Anil Malhotra, Marian Malone, Helen Monaghan, Christine Monk, Dáirine Ní Mheadhra, Joseph O'Connor, Nessa O'Mahony, James O'Sullivan, Maria Pierce, Peter J. Pitkin, Orna Ross, Fiona Ruff, Peter Salisbury, Eileen Sheridan, Brian Smyth, Peter Smyth, Karen, Conor & Rowan Sweeney, Mike Timms, Olive Towey, Simon Trewin, Ruth Webster, The Irish Centre for Poetry Studies, Lilliput Press, Munster Literature Centre, Poetry Ireland and Trashface Books.

We'd also like to thank those individuals who have expressed the preference to remain anonymous.

By making an annual contribution of 75 euro, patrons provide the magazine and press with vital support and encouragement.

Become a patron online at
www.stingingfly.org
or send a cheque or postal order to:
The Stinging Fly, PO Box 6016, Dublin 1.

issue 24/volume two
Spring 2013

NEW POEMS (CONTINUED)

REVIEWS

COVER ART

Alana Richards

COVER DESIGN

Fergal Condon

'… God has specially appointed me to this city, so as though it were a large thoroughbred horse which because of its great size is inclined to be lazy and needs the stimulation of some stinging fly…'
—Plato, *The Last Days of Socrates*

Next Issue Due: June 2013

The Stinging Fly
new writers, new writing

Editor
Declan Meade

Poetry Editor
Eabhan Ní Shúileabháin

Design & Layout
Fergal Condon

Editorial Assistant
Thomas Morris

Eagarthóir filíochta Gaeilge
Aifric Mac Aodha

Contributing Editors
Emily Firetog, Dave Lordan & Sean O'Reilly

Printed by Hudson Killeen, Dublin
ISBN 978-1-906539-24-5 ISSN 1393-5690

Published three times a year (February, June and October).
We operate an open submission policy. Guidelines are on our website:
www.stingingfly.org

The Stinging Fly gratefully acknowledges the support of The Arts Council/
An Chomhairle Ealaíon and Dublin City Council.

PO Box 6016, Dublin 1
stingingfly@gmail.com

Editorial

It's February and we are accepting submissions this month, which means that in the corner of the office there is a mounting pile of envelopes. It isn't a very big pile yet. Today is only the 12th; the rush is likely to come towards the end of the month. Within the next few days, however—with this issue safely gone to print—I'll start opening those envelopes and taking out the poems and short stories they contain. The process of producing another edition of *The Stinging Fly* will have begun.

We published our first issue in March 1998, nearly fifteen years ago. Given that, in literary-magazine terms, we've practically reached *heroic* old age, it is time, perhaps, to reflect on what has brought us this far. The secret, of course, lies inside those envelopes. (Not in all of them, it needs to be said. In one out of every twenty—or every twenty-five—would probably be closer to the mark.) It is the excitement of finding new writing, and the exhilaration, time and again, of discovering new voices. It is the satisfaction that comes from delivering new work out into the world—having first worked with the writer to make sure that it's good and ready.

The Stinging Fly's time here on earth has coincided with the rise and rise of the Internet, bringing with it a revolution in how we access information and communicate with one another. It has opened up a whole new set of opportunities for readers, for writers, and for publishers. During the first flush of excitement surrounding this new era of seemingly endless possibility, however, it was not uncommon to hear that publishers, also, had the most to lose. Were these gatekeepers needed anymore? Would they not become irrelevant?

My own belief is that, if anything, the ease of access to online and digital publishing serves to reinforce the need for the conscientious gatekeeper, the knowledgeable curator, the thoughtful editor. It is still the editorial process that offers the clearest path. Think of that growing pile of envelopes in the corner. Now where would you like to start?

Declan Meade
stingingfly@gmail.com

Note: We will accept envelopes with submissions again in June and October this year. Submissions received this month will be considered for our Winter 2013-14 issue. Our Summer 2013 issue is a special all-translation issue.

RE:*fresh* | *The Parts* by Keith Ridgway and *The First Verse* by Barry McCrea

Michael G. Cronin

THE STINGING FLY

> '*To articulate the past historically does not mean to recognise it "the way it really was".*
> *It means to seize hold of a memory as it flashes up at a moment of danger.*'
> —Walter Benjamin, 'Theses on the Philosophy of History'

At first glance Keith Ridgway's *The Parts* (2004) and Barry McCrea's *The First Verse* (2008) offer a warning to Irish novelists against setting their work too specifically in the contemporary moment. The social geography of boom-time, early twenty-first century Dublin is so vividly realised in these novels that, in the wake of the economy's precipitous collapse, they must now assume the appearance of period pieces. Better then, the aspiring novelist may surmise, to follow the well-trod path of your senior colleagues, take the long view and construct elegant narratives penetrating the murkiness of family secrets and Ireland's tragic twentieth century.

However, we may also want to consider the alternative, paradoxical view that these two novels actually provide us with a more dynamic, complex perspective on Irish history—than, for instance, that offered in the more popularly acclaimed works of Sebastian Barry, Roddy Doyle, Anne Enright or Colm Tóibín—precisely because they are structured around space rather than around time. In other words, rather than being the literary equivalent of a ghost estate—unsettling reminders of a misjudged turn in Irish writing—these works may point towards potentially fruitful directions for the future of the Irish novel.

The Parts is impossible to summarise succinctly. It is effectively composed of six plot lines. The narrative is broken into different sections, each narrated in the third or second person but focalised around one of six characters. These sections are of widely varying lengths and without any discernible rhythm or pattern to their sequence. Ridgway uses typographical devices to indicate to the reader which character is the focus of each section; an ideogram for five of the characters and a different font for the sixth. Playing with the conventions of narration and presentation in this way, Ridgway displaces not only the unique individual perspective from the centre of the novel but, even more significantly in the context of contemporary Irish writing, dislodges the family, and the idiosyncratic dysfunction of the Irish family, as the basic plot unit and as the most pressing theme in Irish fiction.

These six stories become entwined in various complicated, random, sometimes comic and sometimes tragic ways. In all of this Dublin acts as the fulcrum on which the plots turns. What gives the novel its distinctive verve then is not only Ridgway's finely-tuned comic writing but also the way in which the city is not a static setting but a vibrant mesh of interconnected energy flows. Our view shifts dramatically from the mansion of Delly, widow of a billionaire pharmaceutical tycoon, in the Dublin mountains to the quayside where young Kez works as a rent boy; from The Front Lounge, city-centre meeting place of well-heeled gay men, to The Pony Bar, inner-city meeting place of ruthless gangsters; from the fashionable city-centre road where Barry pays a fortune to live in squalor to the recently gentrified Inchicore, where his boss, Joe, lives in mid-life, middle-class despondency, and from there further out to the working-class estate, to which Kez returns from the city to visit his family.

Opening out the plot in this way—moving between diverse landscapes and planes of experience—the novel gives imaginative shape to the fractured, stratified but thoroughly interconnected social spaces of the modern city. To an unusual degree in recent Irish writing Ridgway's novel powerfully captures the intricate geography of the city's class relations: the circuits of privilege and exploitation endlessly reproducing these divisions; the circuits of consumption ceaselessly generating unquenchable desires; and those transnational circuits of wealth and power embedding the city in the geography of global capitalism—the movement of capital and luxury connecting Delly to Paris, London, Zurich and New York being the obverse of those movements of poverty and migration which bring Joe's Nigerian neighbours to Dublin.

With its conventional first-person narration and teenage protagonist, on the surface McCrea's *The First Verse* appears to conform to familiar staples of Irish writing: the venerable coming-of-age novel and its younger avatar, the gay coming-out novel. A young man leaves his well-off south Dublin home to begin his student career at Trinity, an exhilarating if anxious-making new social and intellectual world opens up for him—including his first forays into the Dublin gay scene and his first relationship. So far, so James Joyce meets Edmund White. However, it quickly becomes apparent to the reader that the central drama of this novel lies elsewhere; over the course of the next year Niall is increasingly drawn away from his new life by his dangerously-deepening absorption in a cult-like relationship with two characters. Together they practise a form of bibliomancy or *sortes virgilanae*; a form of fortune-telling using books—interpreting a randomly chosen line of text to answer a question. In a more advanced form of this practice the three ritualistically read and re-read a selection of randomly-chosen passages until it induces a hallucinogenic or visionary state in them.

So after a while Niall's life consists of nights spent at these occult rituals, and days spent wandering the city—guided, when he wishes to be guided, by doing *sortes*.

As with *The Parts* there is much one could say about this curious, lushly written and wonderfully moving novel, not least as a parable about literary criticism—and it is probably no coincidence that McCrea is also an accomplished literary critic. Just one of its distinctive stylistic features is the recurring description of Niall's wanderings through Dublin (and later in the novel through Paris), which makes use of place names, landmark buildings and the names of actual businesses, and, most strikingly, uses recurring passages in which such place names are listed with rhythmic, incantatory effect. Niall is a contemporary incarnation of Charles Baudelaire's nineteenth-century *flâneur*; the detached yet engaged wanderer of the modern cityscape, whose apparently leisured, aimless movements mask a more serious purposefulness; the figure that for Walter Benjamin embodied the peculiar excitement and alienation of urban modernity. But more than this, the style of the novel means that we do not merely observe Niall on his travels but actually experience something of the *flâneur's* ambiguous perspective; caught between the soothing reassurance of place names, with their promise of solidity and permanence, and the discombobulating effects of movement and ceaseless flux.

The Russian literary theorist Mikhail Bakhtin coined the term 'chronotope' to describe the use of space and time in fiction, and in particular the use of literary figures or tropes which productively merged these dimensions. As Bahktin put it: 'in the literary artistic chronotope, spatial and temporal indicators are fused into one carefully thought-out, concrete whole. Time, as it were, thickens out, takes on flesh, becomes artistically visible; likewise space becomes charged and responsive to the movements of time, plot and history'.

Ridgway and McCrea use the city as such a chronotope in *The Parts* and *The First Verse*, and so their novels generate a volatile historical dynamic—arguably, more complex and challenging than those contemporary Irish novels directly concerned with the Irish historical experience. Despite their subtlety, nuance and rigour the historically-oriented novels of Barry, Doyle, Tóibín and even Enright—despite her acerbic, satiric parries at Celtic Tiger aspirations—invariably carry the risk of encouraging a certain complacency about the present; as the destiny to which history has delivered us, so much better than all that dark stuff in the past, and probably the best that we can hope for.

By contrast these two novels generate a sense of history as an ongoing struggle between contending forces. In each the geography of the novel, as both a thematic and as a structuring device, is crucially connected with the themes of chance and control. The movement of the plot is predicated on a notion of the city as a space where the individual is at the mercy of random events, coincidences and synchronicities. Yet the novels also suggest that there is some system or structure at work, one that may not be controlled or fully grasped but against which one can nevertheless wage a struggle.

In *The Parts* there is much grimly comic satire on the values and mores of the 'Celtic Tiger'—as well as satire on the endless critical commentary about the values and mores of the Celtic Tiger. Hence the extended description of Barry preparing for his date—his highly elaborate grooming and dressing, the insistent naming of the brand labels on his clothes, shoes, fragrance—comically indicts a culture where self-fashioning has been so rigorously commodified, while also gesturing knowingly at the cultural stereotype of the vacuous, fashion-conscious gay man. Nevertheless, Barry also meets Kez and, despite himself, falls in love with him. But then, through the complex working out of the plotlines, loses him again. Thus the novel offers us a sense that connection—albeit fragile, partial, compromised—is still possible, or at least still imaginable.

In *The First Verse*, Niall's abject descent because of his immersion in the *sortes* allegorises the alienation of modern life. Incidentally it also suggests that the proliferation of new communication technologies has frayed rather than strengthened connection, making it easier to become isolated; because Niall remembers to send the odd text or make an occasional phone call to his parents they don't come looking for him or realise how his life has been so altered. But even though his addictive immersion in the *sortes* is diminishing and disabling, and the cult-like organisation (which may or may not exist) has a sinister feel to it, the novel also attests to the desire for something beyond the real, beyond the world as it is now. The name of the organisation—PMV, 'Pour Mieux Vivre' ('To Live Better')—is heavily ironic, given its effect on Niall's life, but suggestive nevertheless. Similarly, we might note the effect on Niall of the ritualistic reading of the texts—hearing music and experiencing visions; in other words, the intimation of another sphere, another range of possibilities. The novel clearly emphasises that the pursuit of such visionary experiences through reading is a secular version of the religious impulse and to be mistrusted—and yet the utopian aspiration for something beyond life as it is lived now is also given full credit.

In short, what makes these novels so interesting, and so promising as exemplars for the future development of the Irish novel, is that they suggest a way of imaginatively responding to history in fiction that carries the potential to render that history into a resource for transforming the future.

Strange Country

Our Greek friend told me that in his country
one funeral is not enough.
The body is dug up in six months' time.
Maggot-stripped bones are put
in a box and slid into the stone shelf

of an ossuary. The family is gathered
together again. This, the ritual
his mother and sister love.
At last or for once I entertain the thought
that maybe women wanted it:

to be the earth to which all bodies
are returned by interment.
That persistent uttering of the womb-tomb
scenario—we couldn't have said it better
ourselves, might have said it

ourselves. And why not take it all
on, redeem our shortcomings?
The gurglings of our psyches
and our most haphazard
remarks made visionary:

A woman blessing a fence,
tapping first this part
then another, then the grass
at the post, stepping away
to pass by, coming back to tap more.

My pelvis shifting—the pain
of your thrust like a memory
of a child's head trying
to escape, a memory
that hasn't happened yet.

The seanchaí's tale of the bountiful cow
wandering off to die
reprinted in the paper and read out over breakfast
like a horoscope for all born
under the sign of ingrate.

Even still, a distant relation's letter
about her son's disease—
When I look at his suffering,
I think of what our Blessed Mother
must have gone through—

makes me wonder who
'our blessed mother' is,
and try to remember
who this woman's
mother is, to me.

We fail to grasp even the usual
symbolism or become self-important.
And when asked to explain why
all the trouble over the six counties
while eating meat-laden salads

in America you said of the Queen—
We must remember that most
of the word symbolic is bollicks.
Of course. The Greeks have double
funerals because of a space shortage.

The woman with the fence is mad.
The cow story couldn't happen in real life.
And yet you drove me to the stream,
the stream that held your mother's ashes,
on the day I arrived in this strange country.

Kimberly Campanello

Beatsploitation
an extract

Kevin Curran

The bus is warm and sweaty. I'd love to open a window and let some air in but most of the kids are wet, their clothes, tracksuits and jerseys soaked through. Hair normally spiked, massaged into strict attention, is shiny and flat on foreheads. No one thought of bringing a towel. You'd expect them to be subdued. But they're wired, buzzing. There's loads of music blaring from their phones. They've won their first game. We've won our first game. We kept a clean sheet. Well, Kembo kept a clean sheet. The slap of the ball off his hands for some of the saves made people wince. He had no gloves. He was immense. Everyone was impressed.

Kembo sits up the front of the bus, across from me and away from the banter and mayhem down the back. There's no one in the seat directly behind us. We're the only ones facing forward. He's humming a tune to himself and drumming a beat on his leg. The rest of them are turned to the back row and the nonsense that's going on there.

'Enjoy yourself?'

'Yeah. It was greah. Shudda brought a towel. But it was greah.'

'You shudda brought gloves, never mind a towel. You can't play in future without them. The ref won't let you.'

He just mumbles so I try to cheer him up by going, 'Do you play for a team? You should ye know.'

'I do sir,' he says, 'the school team.' He smiles proudly at his new revelation and turns to look out the window, into the condensation and the streaks of water. The noise from the back row rises.

'S-s-sir,' he says after a while, still looking out the window.

'Yes, Kembo.'

He grimaces as he struggles with a question. His lips pout and he turns to me.

'Wh-why do I haveta wear the grey jersey?'

'I don't get ye.'

The bus bounces on a pothole. Loud cheers fill the back.

'The top I w-wear. Wh-why do I haveta wear it? Everyone else like, wears the purple n white jerseys.'

More cheers down the back. I stand up and peer down at them. I spot someone standing on the seat and give a roar.

I return to Kembo. His eyes are open wide, waiting on my reply.

'Cause yer the keeper—you have to wear a different colour jersey.'

He tuts and shrugs and frowns as if I've disappointed him. He looks again to the window and goes, 'Then I don't wanna be a keeper.'

'Ye see Kembo, you're different from the rest cause you can handle the ball—the referee needs to see who's the keeper so you have to wear a different colour jersey. Yer made to be a keeper. It's the most important position.'

'Oh,' he says, letting my words wash over him. It's a slow acknowledgement that lasts until his breath dies away. He falls back into his seat, sighing slightly, and runs his fingers down the glass. The raindrops shoot across the pane and split into separate strands. Water surges forward in the rubber grooves at the bottom of the window.

Some time later he says, 'Sir?' and I turn to him, getting tired of his calling, but giving him a chance since he played so well.

He continues to look out the window. Silence.

'Em, nothing,' he says, shaking his head.

I know there's something, but don't respond or press him and turn back to my own thoughts. Then, again, it comes.

'Sir?'

And again I turn and say, 'Yes, Kembo,' and this time he does go on.

'Me mama doesn't like me playin football an stuff.'

Never saw this coming.

'And…'

'Sh-she thinks I'm just doin it to miss class like, and sh-she says I don't even, like I'm no good so I should stay in school an, an not miss class cause it'd be bad for stuff. So—so this is like, sh-she doesn't know like. I can't play after this.'

I blow out a short breath to give myself some time. I can't lose him too. We'd be finished without him. I'd lose all the potential half days. I need those breaks.

'Ye know what I was thinking,' I say.

'Mmmhh?' he says, still looking out the window.

'Captain, don't we need a captain.'

He comes away from the middle distance and turns his head to me, lifting it up as if to say 'Go on.'

'How would ye feel if I made you captain?'

His cheeks lift. His eyes smile.

'Yeah. You'd never not be part of the team then would ye? And yer ma couldn't say you weren't any good then, could she?'

His bottom lip comes out and he shrugs. The bus growls and lumbers around a corner.

'Go up for the toss, and lead the team and everything.'

'Serious?'

'Yeah.'

'Would I get my thingy, my picture in the paper an stuff?'

'If we do well, yeah, defo.'

He nods to himself as if it's sorted.

I call them from the front of the bus, over the laughing and the engine, the wind and the rain. The driver turns the radio down.

'Lads,' I say, 'well done today. Great game. Great game.'

They cheer.

'Right. I've decided on a captain.'

A few of them jump up and offer their services. The others laugh.

'Okay, sit down. I thought our defence was brilliant today—the whole back four and the keeper.'

'The black four…' Abdel shouts, and they all burst out laughing.

Kembo appears beside me.

'Don't say that. T-t-that's stupid.'

'But it isn't,' Abdel says, shaking his head, 'me and Kembo an Nifemi an Jordi are all black—we're the black four.' More laughter.

'Wha abou me?' JJ says, his white face popping up from behind a headrest, 'I'm not black and I'm a defender.'

'The back four were excellent,' I say, ignoring it, 'and I thought Kembo in particular was excellent and led by example—so he's our new captain.'

The windscreen wiper squeals as it crosses over. Brows go deep and there's mutters; a Mexican wave of disgruntled tuts spread from the back seat up. Whispers and secret looks follow. The engine struggles up a hill and I go to say something but Kembo goes, 'Ih-if I'm your captain we'll win—an we'll beat the Community College.'

A voice, hidden behind a headrest goes, 'That's g-g-great,' and little sniggers swallow up the joke.

'Enough,' I shout and go, 'so for the next game—Kembo's captain. Okay?' Mumbles. 'Okay?' More mumbles. I leave it at that.

They leave the bus quietly, the buzz of winning drained away. I pat each of them on the shoulder as they go and say, 'Well done.' They don't respond. Their mess, crisps and cans mixed with brown water and feet marks, remain.

Kembo is waiting for me at the school gates, his bag over his head, sheltering from the rain. He puts out his hand.

'Let me take one of your bags, Sir,' he says.

'No way. You've done enough today. Go on home—go on. You'll get sapped.'

The last thing I want's a hug or something. Can't be too careful.

He shakes his head, the bag swaying from side to side, and takes the kit bag. I shift the bag with all of the bibs and footballs on my shoulder and we walk away from the gate, down the slope, past the misty pitch beside the gym and into the empty school. I ask him to leave the bag inside the main door and shake his hand and say thanks and well done and move away from him. He nods, a new seriousness on his face, the water dripping from his nose. He stretches his lips and looks into the distance, just like on the bus, makes to move, stops and then moves towards me. He looks troubled.

'Go on ye mad thing,' I say, making light of the new awkwardness.

He doesn't move.

'Everything okay?'

His kit bag is his school bag. It drips on the tiles when he spins it.

'Do ye want me to pass something on to the Guidance Counsellor?'

I hope he doesn't. I wanna catch my train. He looks at me, finally, with a new determination. I think of that punch.

'Can you write…'

'Course I can write.'

He smiles and chuckles to himself, 'No, can you write me a letter?'

'A letter?'

'A letter.'

'Okay, cool. For what?'

'My mama w-w-wants me to get a letter from the school and stuff like, to say that I'm a good s-student. I need it like. We need ih like, to show we're like doin well.'

'A letter. Cool.'

'For immigration like. They need proof an stuff. Is that okay, Sir?'

'No problem. Good man.'

I pat his shoulder and feel his damp jacket. I think of the two of us at the door. His face.

'Thanks, Sir.'

Still there's no mention of it. Will there ever be? I wonder if he's holding it over me, for a time when I say no to him, a time that could've been today.

He opens the door and puts the school bag over his head but then takes it away and strolls out into the rain, easily, as if the clouds have disappeared and the gloom has been lifted.

*

Even though I grew up in this town, I don't know it anymore. The train station is a three minute walk from the school—I know, I've timed it. My eyes only see the ticket machine, the beach behind the station, the path from the station, the road beside the school, Supervalu across the road from the school, and the big wooden hoarding, remnants of once-started, still-not-finished 'summer works' that hide the school from the town like a dirty secret.

There's a problem with walking though. The school has one main entrance. The entrance beside the pitch, the entrance all the cars take, and the students walk through, is the only entrance. The problem with this entrance is that it's on the opposite side of the school to the train station. So I have this key, to unlock a mad thick padlock, hooked onto a heavy chain, which is hooked onto a bolt that is set deep in the wooden builder's hoarding that encloses the front of this side of the school.

Everything, according to my da, has changed in the town. But I don't see any of this change around the beach.

'I suppose,' he says, peering up past me, making sure the road is clear before he pulls out, 'the beach seems grand in passing, son. I mean, to the untrained eye.'

I'm in the passenger seat of me da's car. Giving him a hand with something.

'Well, the lighthouse and the harbour look good. They've been done up, haven't they?'

The train station backs up onto the beach. Looks out across the sand, out to the sea, and if I stare hard enough, I can see my parents' estate, on a hill, up and away from the lighthouse and the harbour.

'The beach is the face of the town, son,' my da says, we're moving now, 'they've got to keep that tidy. They should do something about the knackers drinking down there though. It's not safe.'

'Yeah?' I try to sound interested.

'It's not right,' he says. I don't think he even heard my question. 'Knackers. Scumbags. The whole lot o' them,' he shakes his head, indicates, changes gear. 'I mean gone's the time meself and your mother used walk along the promenade and down into the sand, and sure, there's gangs of young lads now.'

'Yeah?'

He nods, a rueful nod, his lips pressed.

'But sure it's that end of the town, son. You must see it yerself. They can't build where we are—thank God—cause of the beach and all that, the cliffs, although Eddie Byrne says they've tried for planning permission for the sailors' cottages and what not. But they won't get that. Too much corrosion and weather damage to the cliffs. But, by Jesus, they've built everywhere they could—and they're still building where they can down your end.'

'My end?'

He grimaces, as if I've asked a silly question. Never had any patience.

'Your end—the opposite end—your school end. Have ye not gone for a walkabout up there? Have ye no interest? Jesus, it's like Beirut.'

'Really?' I say, just so he doesn't think I'm not interested. He looks at me out the side of his eyes, 'Sure why would ye care, you live in town, this town means nothing to ye. All ye did was get reared here. Sure what's the town ye grew up in to the likes of you. But let me tell ye, son, it's a sad day the day ye forget where ye grew up—d'ye hear me? Don't forget where ye grew up, where your family's from, where ye teach, where yer childhood friends live, where your parents' friends live, and drink.'

I sigh and feel embarrassed for something I can't quite put my finger on. It feels like I've one of those redners I could never get rid of when I was a teenager. Shame and anger with something elusive. Fair play, Da. Been a while.

'I don't forget where I'm from. Sure how could I?' I say, 'how far away is Hopper's house from here da? I've got to get a train.'

We've passed the station. It's half four.

'I suppose the train's costing ye too,' he goes, ignoring the question, 'I don't see why ye can't live here in town, the community, be part of it son. How's the town meant to hold itself together if there's no sense of community anymore?'

He stares ahead, at the road, but into it too, into some other place I can't see. He glances at me and frowns like he's battling with something. His eyebrows dig deep, 'Just, son, pride. All I'm askin is ye take some pride in your work—where ye work, and where yer from. Don't forget you're representing your parents, son, when ye work up there.'

'Why ye sayin this, Da?' I say, losing patience, 'what've ye heard?'

We stop at traffic lights. The air coming from the heaters, clearing the windscreen, blows between us.

'I'm just sayin. People do be sayin things too, ye know.'

I shake my head.

'People say things, son. Ye know this place as well as I do. Ye fart at the church and they have ye soilin yer pants again the story reaches the canal.'

'And?'

He breathes a heavy sigh, indicates, and we move onto the main street, the old main street; the 'For Let' signs and the African hairdressers—two in a row—the 'Afro Caribbean' restaurant above the boarded-up pub me and Jen met in, the dry cleaners where the IRA had their headquarters in 1920 when Lawless and Gibbons were stabbed to death by the Tans, two 'Cash for Gold' joints facing each other across the main road—one-stop shops for all the thieves in the area—the shell of a Tesco, waiting on a new shopping centre to be completed up the far end of the town—a mall of the future—before it closes. We pass the school, the hoardings, the door, my main-street entrance, and keep on going. We pass the council estate on our right, the cop shop on our left, into an estate I used to drink in when I was sixteen. But we're on a new road, a big major road type thing, and the estate I used to drink in, the fields we'd hide the booze in, are gone and we're driving on, heading towards what looks like a new town. What I once knew ends after the first roundabout and what were once fields are vast estates. We drive through the narrow streets, like old medieval village paths or something, and I begin to see the new town my da's been talking about, complaining about. A playground, houses with no gardens. No garden walls to chat over, no porches, no space. Just doors and cars up on kerbs. Where once there must've been white paint shining from the buildings, there's a yellowy type of grime. That's what you get when you have tenants, not owners. They're never going to go out and paint something that's not theirs. The people on the path, at the doors, in the green Puntos passing us, are mostly foreign—mostly black.

We keep driving. My father just lets me take it all in. It's too much. Not the spectacle, but the buildings. There's a cramped kind of feeling as if the houses were thrown up, on top of each other, dumped there, just so they didn't have to go somewhere else and deface a nicer town. After a few more turns and a few more groans from my da, we reach what must be the centre of this new collection of roads.

A pub, a supermarket, a Chinese, dry cleaners, café, pizza joint, chipper, newsagent's, beauty salon and a hairdresser's. It's not like a new town up here. It *is* a new town up here. Free and independent of the place where I grew up.

'Ye see, son,' my da says, finally coming out of his silence, 'this is what we're up against now.'

I don't know who the 'we' is and who they're 'up against'. I just nod.

'Don't forget where ye come from.'

'I won't, Da. I don't.'

'That end of the town,' he says and nods back, to his left, back to where we've come from, 'remember your own.'

'My what?'

He sniffles, checks his sides and moves off, 'Yer own. Remember who to look out for in the school. People talk. Again you've done something for someone, there'll be two that'll be sayin you did something against them and be bad mouthin ye to those that'll listen.'

'Who's sayin what, Da?' I say, wishing he'd just get to the point. But that's how he works. He speaks while his head slowly shakes, 'Just people,' he says, 'don't forget where yer from—that's all. People down our end talk, son.'

'Talk about what, Da?'

'This end.'

'This end?'

He nods to a black man passing by.

'Oh,' I say.

'Just, look after yer own,' he says and turns on the radio to some drive-time show and we leave the unnecessary turns and long-winded tour of the town and return to the main street.

We arrive at Hopper's house and I see the ladder lying in the long grass of his front garden and hope we can get this done quickly, loaded, tied up and be ready to go in five. My train's in fifteen minutes.

'Isn't it well for some,' Hopper says nodding at me, but talking to my da, 'I wish I had the free time our lad has here.'

'I see you're off today, Hopper,' I say and me da looks at me all annoyed. Hopper hasn't worked in years.

'How's he getting on below?' Hopper says, obviously talking about me, but facing me da, as if he's the expert. They exchange a sly glance. The question is loaded with some other meaning I'm obviously not clued in on.

'Grand,' me da says and then, from the porch, a figure comes out, still and subdued.

'Ah, Andrew,' my da goes, 'Jesus, you're getting bigger every time I see you. What year ye in now?'

'Fourth,' I say.

My da looks at me and smiles, 'Don't tell me you have this monster, Andrew, have ye?'

Andrew nods a bashful nod. 'English,' he says. It's weird seeing him without his two cronies: The Droogs.

'Oh, he has him alright,' Hopper says, lifting up the ladder, 'my Andrew could tell ye some stories. Hates the place—but sure—the goings on up there I wouldn't blame him.'

And there's that look again, from Hopper to me da to Andrew. An unspoken look of acknowledgement, as if I'm missing out on something, not part of the gang. In fairness though, I'm glad. Whatever gang they're in, I don't want to be part of it.

Andrew brushes past me into the garden, where himself, Hopper and me da pick up the ladder and bring it to the trailer at the back of me da's car.

'D'ye need a hand?' I shout after them, wondering why I was even brought.

My da struggles with the ladder but looks up briefly and says, 'No, son, you stay there and watch us. Sure Andrew is here to help, thank God.' So I stand there like a tool and watch while they work away without me.

'You playin ball at all?' me da goes.

'No,' Andrew says, all eyes on the ladder, 'couldn't even make the school team and they were short a goalkeeper an all. They've all sorts playin for them now, even captain.'

'Yeah?' my da goes and looks to me. There it is. I'm about to say, 'You're too old for the team, Andrew,' but don't bother. I know the conversation's not about him.

FEATURED POET

Clare McCotter's haiku, tanka and haibun have been published in many parts of the world. She won the IHS Dóchas Ireland Haiku Award 2010 & 2011. She has written numerous articles on the work of the Belfast-born novelist and travel writer, Beatrice Grimshaw. Her poetry has appeared in *Abridged, Boyne Berries, Crannóg, Cyphers, Irish Feminist Review, Revival, The SHOp* and *The Stinging Fly. Black Horse Running*, her first collection of haiku, tanka and haibun, was published in May 2012. Home is Kilrea, County Derry.

For Your Secrets

I will construct a reliquary of silver and crystal.
In a small chapel beyond bone and stars
it will be placed under the ormolu eyes
of the white night bird your guardian figure.

I will ask no question of provenance or authenticity
attend no pilgrimage or holy-day procession
but at dusk listen until all is quiet
then pour your mysteries into the casket's core.

I will keep each one far from monk and monastery
simony and reforming silversmith.
Crossing fields at midnight for a silent mass
sole celebrant touching a globe of opaque glass.

The Emerald Swallow

for Patricia Bartlett

Speaking to you of the emerald swallow
in a dusty shaft of pool-room sun
he discusses family tradition
grandfather got one on Gibraltar
father leaving The Crum.
Turning talk to victims to terms of parole
you're no soft child.

Speaking to you of a tall ship
sailing in tangled moon
he says only ever a single ambition—
drive a Scania forty tonner long distance
but how could a fucking dickhead
with a record
get a HGV Class One?

Speaking to you of love and hate
the first skin shrines
he recalls a teacher's reaction
two words you can actually spell.
Asked to read in front of others
straight out the door
telling the baldy bastard go to hell.

Speaking to you of the blue banner
unfurling a mother's name
he mentions that night
she did it right.
Curled in pink on the bathroom floor
fistful of Temazepam
quarter bottle of Smirnoff.

Speaking to you of time management
the suit says six minutes
per offender interview.
Two hours for complete report.
But tonight you know
after five thousand miles
a green bird glides
over the field of the ancient wheat
after five thousand black glistening miles.

In the Field of Shells

in memory of Annie McGill (née Bradley)

Fixed in a Box Brownie's
ghostly heart your silence soughs
leaves silvering each snap
shot at a front door
closed on three small rooms
housing eleven.
His lime-wood fiddle hanging
near the lintel.

Threshold he crossed nightly
brown brindled hound at heel
calling on cronies
or Hayworth and Hedy Lamarr.
Leaving hearth little left to burn
save foggies you gleaned
on bracken bog
in a white deer moon.

Later your good girls' slim
factory pay packets
bought the winter coat worn
during vigils kept.
Times with a granddaughter
stock-still by your side
wondering yet what sent you out
to that huckster shed.

Inscrutable camellia face
petalling the fragile earth
as a ribbon of night
twines upland grasses.
Skylark and lapwing
and golden plover nesting
where your silence spooks horses
in the field of shells.

Clare McCotter

Wind Flower

Before shade becomes too dense under thorn
and ash and oak and elder
the anemone opens its arms
to a scrawny sun
unsettling in early April as a road or womb.

Month I called all those years ago
from a graffiti daubed booth in North Belfast
anticipating perhaps wanting
some kind of reprimand
still stunned having just jacked in the job.

Night nurse in private health care setting
or as a patient
from the Shankill said fucking kip shop
taffeta-tongued owner with a padlocked till
age commoditised & dementia hawked.

Ringing that morning expecting mention
of bill and mortgage
your only words sure it's the spring
season when the shy wind flower wakening
at dawn waits for its wild and fickle god.

Now with sepal and stem and lobed-leaf gone
lone woodland trace is a root mound
but the phone box survives
and in cold crystal air a single white star
shaped flower blossoms there.

Clare McCotter

After Poetry

'Poetry is dying. That is why I had to make the film...
The two become one through the poem.'—Lee Chang-dong

You tell the doctor nouns
are more important
she replies
in dementia first to go
person, place, thing
hiding out where
tall wild iris
fasten their blue kimonos
in a garden of stars.

She talks to you of tides
nothing can turn
not even the bleached bones
of a winter moon
as shyly you unfold
your sole ambition
just one poem
one silently waiting
in a heart of pure amethyst.

Darkening as you study
each cicada cry and swollen
in your hand
an apple's waxed shadow
and on pine a patch
of moth-shaped light
calling like a last letter
in warm neighbourhood
sodium night.

In the gold of the morning
your moment comes
on ground summered
with fallen apricots
and speckled grasses
path a girl walked
each day to high orchards
tracing the lost liniments
of her father's face.

After poetry your search
not suicide
following footprints
to the water
beginning to dream
before wide black water
opens its arms
to your embrace
and finding her there
among the crimson
chrysanthemums
light a candle in the grave.

Clare McCotter

The Dead Blue Tit

On its back under raw rafters
cloud facing claws curled around
thin stems of light
the precise beak compassed
towards a path
it saw coming through wild birch
and wild lowland bog
that November they placed
a For Sale sign
at the house built on ground
where you lived as a child
with a mother
and father dead years
before developers
came to collapse an old home
on its wide grey skirts.

Dust billowing from frayed hems
mingled with new mortar
you want to own
but worried the dead blue tit
weightless on your palm
is a creature of ill omen
portending some sly snare
rather than message
sent to an only daughter
from one who knew
the places birds go to die
free from storm and predator
and if left unburied there
flesh and blood and bone gone
with the skylight's fold of stars
decay transmuted to feathers
trembling in blue topaz and gold.

Clare McCotter

Jeopardy
Nora Pyne

'For $400, this president was assassinated while attending the play, *Our American Cousin*.' 'Lincoln,' says Muriel, not bothering to look up from her crossword. That was the softball easy question. She knows the other answers already; there are only so many assassinated presidents. You either know them or you don't. The contestant on the TV, a postal clerk from Lexington, Kentucky, looks like she might. 'For $600,' the host asks, 'this president was assassinated at forty-six, making him the youngest president to die in office.' 'Kennedy,' says Muriel, pencilling *Madras* into the spaces on the crossword, but writing *Madrid* in the margin, just in case. She and the postal clerk keep going. 'For $800, this president, assassinated in 1901, was the last US president to have served in the Union Army during the American Civil War.' Good clue, thinks Muriel to herself; 'McKinley,' she says to the TV. The postal clerk gets the answer. 'For $1000, this president, assassinated in 1881, was shot just four months into his term as president.' 'Garfield,' they both say, while Muriel writes the word *komatik* in the crossword. The show goes to commercial and Muriel gets up to make her tea.

*

'For $1000, this Roman emperor was both the great-great grandson of Julius Caesar and the star of this 1979 cult film.'

The 1979 Northwest Lutheran Women's Convention was held in Billings, Montana. Over thirty ladies from Muriel's church alone, more than any other church in town, enough so that they had their own bus for the drive across the state. She packed the freezer with three days' meals for her husband Chester; the last of their children had just left home for college. The ladies on the bus told jokes and sang the old songs the whole way from Parkton to Billings. The trip alone was enough for Muriel; she loved the picnic lunch at Glacier National Park, all those rolling hills of wheat and the bison grazing near Great Falls. The convention theme was 'Women and Family' and the worship uplifting. Pastor Boffmann, the keynote speaker that year, had the ladies energised by the end of his closing address. All those bake sales and layettes for the poor, and education packs sent with the missionary service to foreign countries, that wasn't empty; it was humanity. Muriel was proud to be Christian.

The other ladies felt it too. It was all so good and happy and honest, in the old-fashioned sense of the word. Norma Bonquest suggested they go paint the town red after dinner. 'No husbands and just us gals!' Norma had said, and Muriel felt as free as a teenager again, walking arm in arm with her best chum to the Saturday matinees or going to an afternoon tea dance with the gang. They met in the lobby, a few ladies from other churches coming along. It was a June evening, Muriel remembered, warm, and crickets chirping outside. Ellen from the church choir was still alive; the cancer had started, but no one, not even her, knew that yet. Muriel and Ellen had always gotten along so well; their kids were the same age and the two families shared Cub Scouts and Brownies, traded skates as kids got bigger, and went to the lake together in the summer. Muriel and Ellen could walk into each other's kitchen without calling first. It was Ellen who was next to her on the sidewalk that evening, and Muriel can still recall the smell of the flowery perfume Ellen took from her purse in the hotel lobby, spraying just a little on her wrists and rubbing them together so her warmth would hold the smell. When Ellen died the next summer, Muriel tried to find that smell again, going the morning after the funeral to the big department store downtown, and walking slowly around the perfume counters with her mouth tight, aware the salesladies were carefully ignoring her, but Muriel didn't care one bit.

On that evening in Billings, everything was still perfect. Kay Mayes, up front, told her joke about Saint Peter and the Norwegian pastor from Seattle, and when she messed up the punchline, they all laughed anyway. Ellen slipped her arm in Muriel's and they walked the rest of the way to the ice cream parlour like that, Ellen and her perfume, Muriel and her happiness.

It was still only seven thirty when everyone had finished their ice cream; some headed back to the hotel to finish packing and get to bed, but Muriel was thankful when Norma Bonquest said the night wasn't over yet.

Later, when Muriel told the story to her bridge club, she stressed that not one of them had known. 'We thought it was a historical drama,' she said. 'It was such a nice theatre and just across the street. With a title like *Caligula*, what would you expect?' The other three women paused, cards held tight. 'So,' said Catherine, 'what was it?' Muriel leaned forward, carefully, giving the words the seriousness they deserved: 'A porno.' 'No!' they had all said, shocked, and Catherine, subbing for Betty who was having her cataracts done, said 'What did you do?' 'We sat through it, every last bit!' Muriel said, still indignant. 'We had paid for our tickets and the manager refused to give us a refund. What else could we do?' The other three women, all young brides during the war and each knowing the value of a penny, nodded their heads in agreement.

*

The winter was a long one and it is still only February. Joe, her son who never married, came home for Christmas, so she had some company for a few days, but her other kids had all moved away years ago, and they had married and had kids in their new cities, and now even those kids, Muriel's grandchildren, were starting to marry and have their own children. Everyone was so far away. They were good, her kids; everyone took a turn coming to visit Muriel for a week or so every couple of months. She thought they must have a script they shared, each one always saying the same thing; 'Mom, don't you think you'd be more comfortable in Riverview? They can look after you there.' But no, she didn't think she'd be more comfortable in Riverview. She had her things and her things were in her house and her house was in her yard and her yard was in her neighbourhood and her memories were in all of those places. In Riverview you got a room, and a room wasn't big enough for a life's memories. Riverview was for old people ready to die, and while she was old, she wasn't thinking about dying anytime soon. Better she stayed where she was. The young couple next door got her groceries each week, and now that the man had retired, he kept her walkway shovelled in the winter and the lawn mowed in the summer. Church sent the minivan on Sundays, the driver coming to the door, helping her carefully across the porch, out to the waiting van and familiar faces. No, she was fine, thank you.

She likes the evenings best, when she knows the whole street is settled in at home, houses warm, supper dishes cleared away, and TVs turned on. It is a comfort to know that each house is doing the same thing. Muriel sometimes looks out through the curtains across lawns to her neighbours' houses, driveways filled with cars and everybody home, porch lights on.

Muriel pulls the TV tray closer to the sofa, gets up and carefully walks to the kitchen, doing the trip in small goals of sofa to television to armchair to kitchen door to counter to oven. She makes herself a cup of tea and takes her time carrying it back to the living room. *Jeopardy* is about to start again. Tea on the TV tray next to the crossword and pencils, carefully easing back down onto the sofa, reading glasses on, TV volume turned up high. For thirty years Alex Trebek in her living room nightly, asking questions while she finishes the crossword and has a cup of tea.

The postal clerk picks the next question. 'Triplets for $1000,' she says, choosing the only unasked question in that column. 'For $1000, these three bones make up the hip.' Muriel looks up.

*

Chester had been a good husband. He hadn't asked too much of her, didn't have any radical thoughts, accepted that the house was her domain, and worked a steady job. They'd married just before he shipped out for Europe, had children when he got back, and when they had enough children, he knew to stay on his side of the bed. He didn't talk about the war and she didn't ask. Chester died a few years after he retired. They'd been able to travel a little in those last few years, and, all in all, he'd been happy with his life.

Things were different during the war. With the men gone, women went out to work. During the four years Chester was overseas, Muriel worked as a shipfitter in the Tacoma shipyards. She loved it. She loved the noise and clang and excitement, she loved the sense of urgency in the work, she loved feeling that she was part of the big effort to win the war, and she believed that what she did was helping to keep Chester safe somewhere over in Italy. When it came time for the harvest back on Chester's folks' farm, she always got special leave to help out Joseph and Agnes for the month. She liked that too. With most of the hired men gone, it was just Chester's mother and father. Chester's brother enlisted and was killed in the South Pacific in May of 1943, but that August his widow Louisa still took the bus from Portland to lend a hand.

For three generations the farm had been in Chester's family, homesteaded by his great-grandparents. It had been tough to keep it going through the war years, but it was tough for everyone, so there was no point in complaining. They were all up with the sun, Agnes cooking for the family and the few hired men too old or too drunk to go to war, everyone out in the fields to bring in the wheat. After supper, the men might spend an hour out in the barn repairing equipment, while in the kitchen, Muriel and Louisa, talking about their lives, put up bottles of preserves and jams from the fruit trees planted long ago outside the kitchen window. Before going to bed, the family sat together in the parlour, Agnes reading the evening prayers. After the final 'Amen', it was an effort for Muriel to climb the stairs on sore feet, change into her nightgown and brush her hair before collapsing in the old double bed, Louisa next to her. 'No need washing two sets of sheets,' Agnes had said, putting them in together to share.

The days and nights moved one into the next, with no sense of where they were in the week, only that there was wheat and sun, then jam and dark and sleep, that the war kept going outside the farm and some or all of their men weren't coming back. Late in the night, two or three weeks into the 1943 harvest, the house had settled into still quiet, except for the sound of her father-in-law Joseph snoring in the next room. Muriel had fallen asleep right away, but now lifted hazily awake, thinking someone was calling her. It was Louisa whispering Muriel's name, Louisa's hand at the back of Muriel's shoulder, and then, after a pause, Louisa quietly closer, hesitant in kissing her neck. Muriel woke into alertness, but with a sense of uncertain panic. She didn't know what to do. Muriel had prepared for her wedding night carefully: she read all of *The Rules and Etiquette of a Married Christian Woman's Life*. 'Between husband and wife there is a special relationship; the duty of a wife is to be patient, understanding that men have certain needs.' In the dark, Muriel thought Louisa smelled of plums, and Louisa's mouth was soft on her neck in a way Chester's had never been. Louisa said Muriel's name again, and moved even closer, her stomach and breasts against Muriel's back. 'A woman has a role as the guardian of the family. Men have physical needs, and women need to be accepting.' Louisa's fingertip traced the line of Muriel's collarbone, shoulder to throat. She whispered in Muriel's ear 'This is my favourite part of you.' They were alone in the dark. Muriel, sick with fear but urgent with something she'd never felt before, took a breath. She rolled over to her sister-in-law.

*

If the night had been cloudy, things would have ended differently. If the moon had been lower, Muriel would have been lost. That night though, the moon was high, with light enough through the window to see shadow. Muriel lay back against the pillows, nightgown pushed up above her waist. Louisa, naked, her feet dangling off the bottom of the bed, rested her head on Muriel's thigh, the taste of Muriel still wet on her mouth. Muriel was about to whisper 'thank you' when she saw the doorknob turn.

In that split second, Muriel saw everything that would happen. She knew what Chester would have to do, and her parents, and her friends, when they found out. Muriel chose to save herself. She kicked Louisa as hard as she could. Louisa tumbled to the floor as Agnes opened the door to check on the muffled noises she'd heard through the wall. Agnes's eyes saw Louisa sprawled naked on the floor, then a second later, Muriel, sitting up in bed, frantically pulling the quilt to her chest over her nightgown. 'It's her! It's her!' sobbed Muriel. Agnes turned back to Louisa, her eyes filled with revulsion, and she slowly said, 'You whore, you filthy, dirty viper. Pack your bag and get out.'

In the morning, Louisa was gone. Agnes never told Joseph, but she told Muriel to always remember to forget what had happened. It was the Christian thing to do.

*

Muriel was confused amid all the smells of Nordstrom's perfume counters that morning after Ellen's funeral, confused lost. It was all so big and so busy. The different perfumes layered heavily in the air as she walked between the counters, a saleswoman at each, pert with thick make-up. Muriel couldn't pick out the individual scents; she couldn't find anything close to Ellen's flowery smell. Burning, musky perfumes for women with shoulder pads clouded the air, closing in, and making it hard for her to concentrate. The funeral had been awful, Ellen's husband silent and unmoving in the pew, so the casket procession couldn't leave the church, and afterwards everyone crowding Muriel to say how sorry they were. Muriel couldn't go to her usual little perfume shop near the neighbourhood grocers. She needed anonymity; she couldn't bear the thought of someone being friendly or familiar or kind to her right now. The perfume section at Nordstrom's was the best idea, but now that she was here, she just couldn't breathe.

*

Kennedy's assassination in November 1963 held Ellen to Muriel's memory. Christmas was subdued and then New Year's Eve arrived. Ellen and her husband hosted the party, determined they would all have fun. Thirty couples squeezed tight into the living room and den, some dancing to a Perry Como record, drinks in hand. Anyone walking in the front door would have said the house smelled like a good time: hairspray, Brylcreem, bourbon, and the midnight buffet, nearly ready.

Ellen was in the kitchen at the stove, carefully transferring cocktail meatballs to a polished chafing dish with the exaggerated concentration of a woman who has had too many highballs. Muriel next to her at the counter, had a small tray in one hand, crackers arranged around a seasonal mousse, the recipe from the latest *Ladies Home Journal*. 'My feet are killing me and pass me the toothpicks, will you?' said Ellen, reaching across Muriel and taking them herself. Ellen eased out of her kitten heels for a second, shoeless feet stretching on the kitchen floor. In the dining room, people were talking about the pictures of Jacqueline Kennedy in *LIFE Magazine*, her brothers-in-law Bobby and Edward at either arm, walking her down Pennsylvania Avenue leading the funeral cortege.

Ellen and Muriel were doing the same, Muriel picking up her drink. 'Imagine it for the poor children, a father gone like that, and Jackie losing a baby only in August.' Muriel knew Ellen was still a bit lost herself after a miscarriage in the spring. She had spent most afternoons that April sitting at Muriel's breakfast table crying. As she spoke, Ellen's hands stopped arranging toothpicks and cubes of cheese. Muriel turned to her friend; this wasn't the time for tears. 'You know what? This girdle feels like I'm trussed up in a python,' said Muriel, and Ellen laughed.

The midnight countdown started on the other side of the kitchen door. 'The girdle's worth it; you look a million bucks in that dress,' said Ellen, and she stepped gingerly back into her heels with a little unsteady sway, reaching a hand out to Muriel's hip for balance. 'Especially here,' she said. 'This is my favourite part of you.' In the other room the midnight cheers started, and impulsively, Ellen, smiling, leaned over, and kissed Muriel's lips. 'Happy New Year,' she said, and Ellen turned to take the cheese tray out to the party, Muriel following a minute later, one woman walking out to kiss her husband, the other to let herself be kissed.

*

At Nordstrom's, that morning after the funeral, Muriel couldn't find Ellen's smell, and she felt herself getting angrier and angrier.

Leslie Bower had started her new job in Cosmetics that morning, perm glossed into place, silver eye shadow arched high. Leslie had not an ounce of common sense but enthusiasm in buckets. That's why the manager sent her out on the floor with a handful of perfume samples. She was the one who stepped in front of Muriel. Leslie sprayed her with the latest signature fragrance. It's difficult to say who was more surprised at what happened. A few minutes later, locked in a cubicle in the ladies room, arms wrapped around her waist, Muriel sobbed in choking gasps, wanting to wail but trying to be quiet. Muriel had slapped the saleslady with the sum of her fury at every bit of unfairness in this life: Ellen buried this morning at Fairmount, and Chester sitting at home reading the newspaper, waiting for Muriel to come home and make his lunch.

*

'Ilium, ischium, and pubis,' says Alex Trebek on the TV, and Muriel, half a century later, can still feel the weight of Ellen's hand on the curve at the top her hip, the force pushing down.

After You Died

I am in Dunnes Stores
thumbing through a rack of wetsuits
trying to find an age-4 for your son.

You are in a rented room in Delhi
smoking and making notes for your latest film.

These days
I am always stuck in Dunnes Stores
trying to find the right wetsuit.
You are always alone in a narrow room,
smoking and making notes.
Your heart is failing but you still don't know it.
It's hard to breathe—for me, as well as for you.
Sometimes I wish I could stop loving you.

≈

I am sitting up in bed,
the cover is black and white stripes.
There are two windows to the room.
In front of me lies the inlet
and a big lump of raw-boned hillside
crowned with soft soggy cloud.
The window beside the bed
frames sky and thin coloured sands
woven with marram grass.
I am thinking of the drawer I opened in my mother's study,
the hundreds of your photos that I found there
from that first India trip.

≈

I dipped Thomas into the waves.
He liked being dipped, he slapped at the water and splashed.
He's one year old and one month.
You've been dead for just seven months.
When I was fifteen I dipped you into the waves.

≈

When I saw the Sydney Nolan picture
of Ned Kelly's sister quilting his black helmet
I knew that's what I'd always tried to do.
A useless love-filled gesture,
the failure of the gesture,
the blood on the blue quilting,
the blood on your face in the morgue.

≈

If it hadn't been India
it would have been somewhere else.
Perhaps I'm glad it was India.
Perhaps I'm glad that your window
opened onto the market.
And over the road, the pigeons,
soft coloured rows in their boxes,
talking in low tumbling voices
drowned out by the roar from the street.

≈

Did you drown in India?
There was the photo of the Ganges,
the liquid light floating the evening water,
the way you broke it as you raised your hand to wave,
the time that you went swimming from the ghats.

Kerry Hardie

This poem is addressed to the artist Paddy Jolley, who died in New Delhi in 2012.
A retrospective of his work will open in the Limerick City Art Gallery in March 2013.

ICU

I'm ready for anything.
Fluorescence, especially, greenly
highlighting distress and vulnerability
with a heartless office efficiency, illuminating
the necessary work of medical technicians
who administer the required invasions
to the checked out body on the gurney and
though it's all for the patient's benefit I understand
you fight them, love, and good for you, good for you.

I'm ready for a gurney as well. Disarray.
The room, the doctors, the nurses, all a shambles,
and you, the guy on the gurney, the one no longer
in charge, matted hair and stained clothes, emblems
of struggle and suffering that happen between
10pm and 3am, between stable and septic,
between polite oxygen mask and rudely forced ventilator,
between your beating heart and your non-beating heart,
just once, for a short time, until they jump it,

in ICU room number one. You're their
number one guy tonight. The one that almost
gets away. Soft grey light, the late summer dawn,
hospitalised, seeps in through horizontal blinds,
revealing hushed technology, stacked tubes
and waving monitors, a nurse absorbed
in charts, recording your vitals (you're still vital),
and in the centre of it all, on a high,
rather comfortable looking trolley bed,

you, focus of the looming mechanical
observers, tucked under blankets that hide
the tubular intrusions, and here's the thing, love,
it's the way they've combed your hair gently over,
no sign of prior struggle, and the absence of
any lines on your face, which is pinkish
under the plastic mask delicately obstructing
my view of the pipe down your throat,
breathed for, stilled, machined into peace.

Cheryl Donahue

Strictly Nil By Mouth

for my brothers

Human interference, the latest in high-tech equipment,
played havoc with the natural navigational sense
of the whale. Less than two metres long,

later weighing more than seven tonne, the whale—
a Beleen, later a Hammerhead—was diverted
from her calling and trapped behind a man-made dam.

All that could be done was being done,
the new Dutch said: their well-meaning advances
designed to tame death, reclaiming more land—

years out there all alone—time and time again
from the sea. No sound made through the throat,
disconnected, reconnected, disconnected,

drip-fed water, malch, news of graduations,
new millennia, grown men, the whale and not death
became the shark in the mind of locals—a terror

assumed to exist but never, never, to be named.
It's unmapped, this new dam built between the whale
and her God in a remote office. Sometimes

in Spring, people passing through the space
her absence makes, report the breach,
then tail slap, of a Blue-Nosed calf sat listening

outside the dam: the long silence broken only
by this incessant *deet deet deet*, little clicking.

Deirdre Doherty

The Art of the Poetic Line

If the wolf-cub clouds clumped for warmth on the sky-like heather
are an excuse for opening with an observation about the weather
I walked in this afternoon, then the later chimney-sweep's broom of
crows endeavouring through the sunset's pumpkin glow to remove
the blockage of shed wolf-hair, by way of perpetual circular
motion, from the towering hollow between the coal-coloured
motorway and the ozone dome must, surely, be seen
as a sight for which memory was made. The crows, I mean:

there was something in their refusal, despite all else, to be end-
stopped that made theirs a state of impossible aspiration,
the best I can hope for being the justified placing
of my hand near yours, something upon which a little must depend.

Adam Crothers

Eustace Madden is breathed upon once more
John Kelly

Eustace Madden is on his way back from the Spar when the Muse, like a flashing swallow from Helicon, anoints him with another idea for a story. The image which comes is perfect and clear—a long-legged hare, in full sunlight, sneaking underneath a wire fence in a barren, dusty field. It is Europe. It is 1944.

Inspiration is a word which Eustace Madden uses freely and he meditates often upon how it seems to *strike*—a sublime power surge that Eustace Madden, while mindful of cliché, can best describe in terms of *flashes* and *bolts*. And now, walking slowly up the hill, the bread and the milk in a blue plastic bag, he is *stricken* again. Or, as the Greeks had it, he is *breathed upon*.

Halting under a cherry blossom, Eustace Madden puts down the bag and allows the image to run. The hares gathering to dip in sequence under the wire. First one. Then another. And then several more, like brown brushstrokes through the scrub. He opens the notes app on his iPhone and starts to tap. Just a few words for now— hares, sunlight, fence, camp. Eustace Madden is thrilled. His talent is tinder about to combust.

A working title follows easily, fully formed and throbbing, and this—*The Hares of Birkenau*—Eustace Madden whispers to himself with gratitude. And then, as he sets off for home again, there's another little *flash* and he renders it more perfect still. 'The Several Hares of Birkenau,' he says aloud, 'by Eustace P. Madden.'

Bernice Madden, who is the wife of Eustace Madden, is swaying like a cobra at the front door.

'Fucksake Bernice,' says Eustace Madden. 'I was only away ten minutes.'

Bernice Madden is eyeing the bag.

'What kind of milk did you get?'

'The kind of milk,' says Eustace Madden, sensing the usual trap, 'that you told me to get.'

Bernice Madden seizes the bag.

'Jesus Christ, Eustace! Do I have to do every fucking thing myself?'

But Eustace Madden, still in the adrenalin rapids of inspiration, grits his teeth, knowing that he must hold tight to *The Several Hares of Birkenau*—the crucial opening lines already forming in his head.

A spring morning in Birkenau. Too bright by far, and the hares—the several hares—are gathering at the fence.

Bernice Madden yanks the bag from Eustace Madden's grip.

'This,' she hisses, 'is full fat!'

A small boy—Max—is watching the hares. They move in that strange hobble which always disguises their speed. Such astonishing speed. And now in the silence of the morning...

'And what the fuck do you call this?'

Bernice Madden takes the loaf from the bag and holds it aloft like some dead brown creature of the wood.

'That,' says Eustace Madden, 'would be a bread.'

And then the story begins to slip. The warm, knobbly bodies of the hares are twisting in mid-air and vanishing into amber particles of themselves.

'And what kind of bread would it be?'

'That would be *brown* bread.'

'And what kind of *brown* bread would it be?'

'I'd say that would be Pat's fucking Pan. I'd say that would be a Pat's fucking Pan whole fucking grain brown fucking loaf.'

'Whole grain?'

'Whole fucking grain.'

'And how many times do I have to tell you that nobody in this fucking house eats whole fucking grain bread?'

The lips of Bernice Madden curl backwards on her face. Teeth and gums are revealed. The brace. The golden canine. And all the pollutant suds of resentment bubbling away on her stubby little tongue. Not, it occurs to Eustace Madden, a cobra's flicker at all. Not a snake's tongue. A frog's maybe. Or a tortoise. And so Eustace Madden grabs the Pat's Pan brown whole grain loaf which nobody will eat and holding it up in front of his wife's hate-filled face, he crushes its vertebrae and shreds and scatters rags of it all over the front garden. And then with the story of *The Several Hares of Birkenau* evaporating like all the others, he pushes over the wheelie bin, calls his wife a mad bitch from Hell, and takes off in rage and determination for the Dart, as if Dún Laoghaire train station might be some portal to another time, another place and an altogether other life.

Forty minutes later Eustace Madden is seated before a pint in Mulligan's of Poolbeg Street. With his preferred pen—a Pilot G1 0.7—he is making notes in his preferred notebook—a black, soft cover, 13x21 Moleskine with plain paper, purchased en route along with Tic-Tacs and an out-of-date copy of the *TLS*. He works fast at times like these, scribbling like some occult Elizabethan trying to fashion the unknowable from a single gifted symbol, the Pilot G1 0.7 moving so fast that he can barely keep up with himself, his calligraphy spreading out like automatic writing, almost Arabesque, page after page until it becomes the score of some avant-garde composer, something even he won't be able comprehend if he leaves it for too long. But Eustace Madden understands that he must write without cease. That he must permit these words, whatever they may be, to splash and to spill so that the very hares of Birkenau will leap from page to page, from the dense scrub and brambles of the left to the pristine snowy field of the right. And it is in these moments, and only in these moments, that Eustace Madden, exhilarated and confident, believes himself to be, however briefly, his actual self.

Eustace P. Madden was born in County Down in 1964. His short fiction has appeared in various publications on both sides of the Atlantic including The New Yorker *and* The Faber Book of Irish Short Stories *edited by Paul Auster. His first collection* The Cobra of Clonskeagh *was shortlisted for the International IMPAC Dublin Literary Award and his controversial memoir* On The Lash With Peter O'Toole *won the Kinsella Prize for Irish Book of the Year in 2013. Now separated from that twisted bitch of a bank official Bernice Madden, he divides his time between Dublin and Paris where he lives with his partner, the novelist, philosopher, model, eroticist, jazz pianist and fetishista, Chantalle Duchamp.*

A quarter of an hour passes and Eustace Madden shouts himself another pint. That stiff pain has returned and he prods at his neck and shoulder as he tries to read what he has just written, his head at an awkward tilt and the Pilot G1 0.7 wavering now between his fingers like an unlit cheroot. Skipping those passages which are already illegible, he gets through the most of it, assuring himself as he deciphers the final lines, that it's not bad at all. *The Several Hares of Birkenau*, he tells himself, will have an energy about it, and an urgent truth. And with the back of it now broken, he'll get up early in the morning and really get stuck in. He just needs to figure out what happens next.

Eustace Madden closes his eyes and pinches the bridge of his nose between finger and thumb. The hares are slipping under the wire. Max is watching them. There is a shot. But does Max die? It seems very early. And is Max perhaps the narrator? Yes, that could be it. The boy is actually telling the story. He is a child ghost now free to play with the hares. In the fields. In the sky even. Or should Max be a living witness? A survivor to whom the hares once gave hope and consolation. In which case Max could be an old man now living in New York in a rent-controlled apartment near Washington Square. Maybe make him a tailor. Or a professor of music. Or is he a famous writer perhaps? That would be a nice touch. An eminent man of letters writing his own story over and over again but writing only about the hares, refusing to mention the prison guards or the SS or any such agents of death because he, as a writer, deals only in life. Or perhaps, instead of New York, he now lives in the countryside so he can be

Eustace Madden is breathed upon once more

near his beloved hares? Or on some island in an Irish lake perhaps, where hares live undisturbed. Isolated. Like Rousseau in *Reveries of a Solitary Walker*—a book he bought second hand years ago and which must surely be full of useful quotes. Yes! Make him a philosopher! An old man who, as a boy, was surrounded by death and who now uses his extreme experience to make sense of life—and of a more natural death. And then of course the hares themselves. All that folklore. Hares as tricksters, as fairies, as witches. The madness of hares. Hares staring at the moon. And so it might even be a story with supernatural elements? Or perhaps a more mystical tale? Like those Borges stories he has taken a few runs at in recent years. And so, yes, *The Several Hares of Birkenau* is a parable of life amidst death. Maybe call the boy something else though? Not so sure about Max any more. It means 'big' but it's such a small word. Distracting perhaps. But yes, what happens next—in the narrative that is—will be crucial.

Eustace Madden, jittery with excitement now, reminds himself as the pints spread satisfaction deep in his soul, that this is why he left Newry all those years ago. Not to work in the Bank of Ireland on O'Connell Street and that's for certain sure. Nor was it to collide with the likes of Bernice Madden (née Savage of the Clonskeagh Savages) at the Christmas party and end up married—*married* for fucksake!—and living in her dead grandmother's house in Dún Laoghaire. Oh Christ the tedium of it! *Sex In the City* and *Cougar Town* and washing down Marks & Spencer's happy meals with chilled Blossom Hill night after fucking night. That knacker blonde feather cut she had. The pink dressing gown. The cold sores. The manky Miss Piggy slippers.

No. It is for solitary moments like this one that Eustace Madden has always been destined. Writing. Imagining. Re-imagining. A real writer now, meditating upon a work-in-progress in a glowing Dublin pub. *This* is why he came to this city! To be sure of himself and of his place fornenst this beautiful and reassuring pint—the definite stout so confident in its black and its white, the glass so cool and solid to the touch. It is for *this* and for nothing else that he came here on an Ulsterbus and never much returned. Eustace Madden arrived in this great city to be a writer of words in this, the very capital of words. Where the track of Beckett's arse is still on every seat. Where the stain of Oscar's ink is still on every Georgian footpath. And where, as one of Eustace Madden's finest lines has it, the wind of Joyce's farts still blooms along the Liffey banks. Eustace Madden closes his Moleskine with a slap and is just about to raise a glass to Bloom, Molloy and all the rest of them when a large bearded man appears at his side.

'Excuse me, sir. I don't mean to interrupt.'

The man is smiling anxiously. Breathing heavily. Cream of Guinness in his whiskers.

'I've been watching you, sir, and I was thinking that you must be a writer. Am I right?'

A Yank. A tourist. And Eustace Madden, as if to indicate urgent business, opens the

Moleskine again. The Yank bows slightly and makes another attempt.

'Forgive me asking, sir, but do I know you?'

Eustace Madden notices how the Yank's moustache seems to sprout from somewhere very deep within his nostrils and he makes a mental note to use this observation in a story. A mountainy man from Donegal perhaps. A defrocked cleric or a cross-dressing ballad singer. Or maybe some flute-making Breton psychopath abroad in West Kerry. Eustace Madden can write those sorts of stories in his sleep. Culchie stuff. Bogs and such. But of course he's beyond that now. His mature vision is deeper than that. His aesthetic more focused and refined.

'Ah no,' says Eustace Madden, 'I don't really think you'd have heard of me. No.'

'Is there anything you might have published that I might find in the bookstore?'

Eustace snaps the top back on his G1 0.7.

'Well, I haven't actually decided to publish anything recently. Not really. No.'

The Yank seems disappointed but the smile returns soon enough.

'Well anyway, sir, you keep up the good work. What is it they always say? Write about what you know. Isn't that so?'

'Go fuck yourself,' thinks Eustace Madden.

'It was nice to meet you, sir,' says the Yank. 'And good luck with the writing. I only wish I had the patience.'

'Even if you had the fucking patience,' thinks Eustace Madden, 'you still wouldn't be able to do it.'

'Thank you,' says Eustace Madden, 'nice to meet you.'

And now, as Eustace Madden sets about his third pint, he decides that he should give some serious thought to the place where his story is set. He's not entirely sure where Birkenau is but there are plenty of books on the subject, and Google too, and maybe in the summertime he might even travel there in order to get the feel of it. And if people can fly from Dublin to Krakow for the weekend and take in Auschwitz while they're there, then maybe he could do that instead? One camp might be as valuable as the next for his purposes. And a direct flight would save him a lot of time and expense. In the meantime, Eustace Madden reassures himself, this is all mere detail for later. Research is only research after all, and the most important element, by far, is the central image—one which he first came across in a biography, or rather in a review of a biography which he had skimmed in the *London Review of Books* some weeks ago (in this very pub as it happens)—some remark about the hares which lived around Birkenau being a symbol of life and continuance, or something along those lines. And he had forgotten all about it until he was walking back from the Spar. Amazing, thinks Eustace Madden, the way it all works. *The spark of an idea.* The unexpected, unlooked for gift of it.

Eustace Madden orders a Jameson and googles Birkenau. Turns out it was part of Auschwitz. He didn't know that. Or that Auschwitz itself was a complex divided

Eustace Madden is breathed upon once more

into three camps with Birkenau (or Auschwitz II) the biggest. In fact Birkenau was the rotten, evil core of the whole thing and Eustace Madden carefully cuts and pastes the word *Vernichtungslager* into the notes app. And now sipping on a second whiskey he decides that *The Several Hares of Birkenau* might turn out be more difficult than he had anticipated. He'll have to sleep on it overnight, let the story bubble a little, and then tomorrow—first thing—he'll knock it all into shape. It would be most unwise, Eustace Madden tells himself, to go at it any further now, all ram-stam and bar-ways. Tone, in a story like this, is extremely important. He will need to be patient and rather more cautious than usual. This is subject matter which must be properly addressed. Honoured even.

The Yank, spotting the Moleskine and the G1 0.7 going back in the bag, approaches with a nervous bow and offers to buy Eustace Madden a drink.

'Oh,' says Eustace Madden. 'Thanks. Well, maybe a pint? Thanks very much.'

The Yank stands to attention as the drinks settle on the bar and eventually he asks if he might sit.

'Go ahead,' says Eustace Madden. 'I think I'm done for the day.'

The Yank sits and offers his hand.

'Stephen J. Flanagan.'

'Eustace P. Madden,' says Eustace Madden.

They shake hands and wait, and it's only when the pints land that the Yank speaks up again.

'You live in Dublin, Mr Madden?'

'Yes. Dublin. Well, Dún Laoghaire. On the coast road. And you?'

'Illinois.'

'Ah, the Windy City.'

'Actually I'm from the Bloomington-Normal area. Originally from Uptown Normal. People tend to find that rather amusing.'

'Uptown Normal?'

'It's where ISU is. Illinois State.'

'You work there?'

'I cut the grass. Somebody's gotta cut the grass, right?'

Eustace Madden raises his glass,

'Best pint in Dublin,' says Eustace Madden. And then he watches as the Yank sinks most of his pint in one long series of gulps.

'Good man,' says Eustace Madden. 'Savour it.'

The Yank laughs and Eustace Madden smiles.

'Uptown Normal. That's a good one.'

More silence until, with a single sweep the Yank gathers his beard to a point and nods towards the Moleskine in the bag.

'May I ask what it is you're writing?'

Eustace Madden shrugs.

'Oh, just something I'm working on. A short story.'

'Short story. Cool. You ever read Philip K. Dick?'

'Are you making that name up too?'

The Yank chuckles.

'He's from Chicago. You haven't read him? You should. Wrote *Blade Runner* and *Total Recall* and stuff like that. *Minority Report*. Or at least he wrote the stories that they based the movies on. You really should check him out. Really, really good. But hey, what do I know? Forgive me but I've been drinking all day and I'm a little buzzed.'

'You're in Dublin.' says Eustace Madden. 'It's compulsory.'

'That's funny.'

'Up to a point.'

The Yank slumps then brightens up in one sudden move.

'So what's your story about?'

Eustace Madden prefers not to talk about his work before it's finished, but he's drunk now and has warmed to the Yank.

'Well, it's kind of about the Holocaust.'

'Jesus,' says the Yank.

'Well it's not just about the Holocaust per se. It's about a small boy and the hares that live on the edge of the camp.'

'You mean like jackrabbits?'

'We call them hares.'

'The Holocaust?'

'Yes.'

'Jesus,' says the Yank again. 'Rather you than me.'

Eustace Madden orders two more pints and as they settle, the Yank tells Eustace Madden about a woman he once knew in Normal, Illinois. A ballet teacher called Miss P whose lawn he cut during school vacations. One sunny afternoon Miss P appeared with a jug of lemonade and it was then that he noticed that she had a tattoo on her arm. A number carved into her skin. He was just a kid, he says, and had no idea what it meant, and it was only a year or two later that Miss P told him her story. How she had once lived with her family in Prague and how in 1942 they were all rounded up and sent to a place called Terezin where they were kept for two years. And that was where she saw Eichmann and looked him in the eyes and all she had to say about him was that he looked very ordinary. And then in 1944 they were all sent to Auschwitz and that's where she got the tattoo. She worked in the laundry and, many times, was put into those selection lines where the women had to take their clothes off and hold them in bundles while Mengele examined their bodies. The women who were passed fit were taken from the Family Camp and sent to the Women's Camp and the old and the sick and the kids were all kept behind. And then at night, Miss P would see the sky

Eustace Madden is breathed upon once more

over the Family Camp all lit up. And this was the bodies burning. Her entire family was murdered. Everyone. And the worst thing about Auschwitz, according to Miss P, was the fact that life itself was a nightmare. That was the very worst part of it. That life itself was a nightmare.

The pints arrive and the Yank stands up. Tears in his eyes.

'Miss P was a real lady. A real lady, you know.'

Eustace Madden immediately brings the fresh pint to his mouth as if to hide himself inside it. The Yank, the tears rolling now, says he needs the men's room and excuses himself and Eustace Madden watches him lumber off, stopping on his way to order two whiskies and indicate their destination with a forefinger which seems to target half the room. Eustace Madden gulps his way through the pint but when the whiskies arrive and the Yank has still not reappeared, he starts to fidget like an altar boy on his first Mass—the two tumblers and the tiny jug of water arranged before him on the table. More minutes pass and still no sign of the Yank and so Eustace Madden suddenly snatches at one of the whiskies and downs it in one. And then, he stands, tilts a little, scatters a few euro on the table, downs the Yank's whiskey, tilts a little more and slips off into the swirling black and amber of the city. Turning into Tara Street, Eustace Madden stumbles sideways against the window of a laundrette and then, righting himself again, he watches a whooping fire engine from Pearse Street make a break for the lights on Butt Bridge.

When Eustace Madden arrives home, Bernice Madden, who is the wife of Eustace Madden, is halfway up the stairs.

'I'm just going for a bath,' she says.

This is a code which, drunk or sober, Eustace Madden can read. Bernice Madden is the kind of woman who likes all things to be clean—the bedclothes, her husband and herself—and a steaming bath tends to be the ritualistic prelude to a rare but surprisingly adventurous session between the warm, crisp sheets. When she tells him that there's wine in the fridge and asks him to bring her up a glass, he is in no doubt. Bernice Madden is in the mood and, as she sometimes puts it, his services are required. And although his belly is swill-full of drink Eustace Madden knows that Bernice Madden, much like the Muse, does not offer herself too often and so he determines to sober up quickly. A big glass of cold water will sort him out. Maybe stick his head out the window for a bit. A stroll in the garden perhaps. In any case, it will give her time to get ready. To soak. To tidy up. To get the gear on. To smooth out the quilt.

And then Eustace Madden hears her voice from above.

'Will you run down to the garage and get some ciggies?'

And Eustace Madden grins. If Bernice Madden wants ciggies then Bernice Madden really is planning on needing one later. He shouts back up to her, high into the darkness.

'What kind do you want?'

'Doesn't matter!'

'Marlboro?'

'Any kind!'

'What if they don't have Marlboro?'

'It doesn't matter!'

'Just tell me what kind you want for fucksake!'

'Just forget it!'

'Just tell me what the fuck you want!'

'Oh fuck off, Eustace!'

When Bernice Madden descends from the bathroom in her pink dressing gown and Muppet slippers, she finds her husband asleep on the sofa, twisted grotesquely on the cushions like a recent corpse. But he's breathing still and, leaning in close, Bernice Madden stares deep into the desiccated hole of Eustace Madden's mouth. Her breath causes her husband to shudder, to wince as if some creature has just crawled across his cheek and Bernice Madden almost smiles. She leaves him to it then. To another night before the unlit fire. His heart hammering, his bladder full to bursting and his hangover brains already swelling against his skull

And so Bernice Madden goes back upstairs with the Blossom Hill and arranges herself, all fragrant and fresh, in her cosy, spotless bed. The first glass is sipped with reverence and, once finished, she immediately pours another, opens her laptop and starts to tap, tap, tap. Tonight she makes the final corrections to her story about a man who has never written a story in his life, a man whose very dreams are astray with failure, judgement and shame. No title yet but the wine might help. And at least it has a beginning, a middle and an end. She'll do what she can tonight, run a spell-check and then read through it once more tomorrow. During her lunch-break perhaps. Or on the Dart. And if she's still happy with it, she'll send it off.

Eustace Madden is breathed upon once more

Through the Eye of a Needle

Still shorter than my hip
but solid, heavy as a scooped-full
coal scuttle, hair so fingerwrapped & knotted
it stands in coils about her ears & won't comb flat,
cherubic, with that dimpled roll of fat above the buttocks
the stubby painted angels carry brightly, her feet & hands a fan
she opens frequently to admire the slotted hinges of her bones,
to blow between the gaps, arm-skin like powder down,
an almost-constant frown atop a round bright box
with treasure in it: seamless lips, even teeth,
eyes that loop the swallows up

on their traceable tethers
to harry them, upside down, into
the huge room of her brain & make them fit
the vivid, random furniture preassembled there—
buttercup petals crushed on her palm, the Teapot Song,
dust motes & the taste of rust, shadows under her cot that grow
vast without a night-light, hunger, always satisfied,
its own fat child in a caul & sleepiness a wall
you dig-a-hole-&-curl-up under—
where they leave their threaded
flight path like the imprint
on a carpet of a stain.

Sinéad Morrissey

Signatures

> *Belfaste is a place meet for a corporate town, armed with all*
> *commodities, as a principal haven, wood and good ground,*
> *standing also upon a border...*

> —extract from a letter to the Privy Council
>   from the Earl of Essex, 1573.

I

Where nothing was, then something. Six months ago
most of this was sludge and a gangrenous slipway
dipping its ruined foot in the sea: a single rusted gantry
marking the spot where a small town's population
of Protestant men built a ship the size of the Empire State Building.
Smashed cars and wreckers' yards flourished in between.

II

A skin-stripping wind. This morning I walk on concrete
smooth as a runway with a full-scale outline laid in light
of the uppermost deck. Railings as over a stern.
Grass. Seating. The memorial for the dead hosts names
I can't pronounce—*Sjöstedt, Taussig, Backström*—
in immaculate glass. Once, I count a surname seven times.

Sinéad Morrissey

Gare du Nord

We sit, looking across at the façade.
When I'm gone, you say, remember
me here. I think about that, imagine
myself alone at this street-side café,
the massive stone of the station filling
my eyes, the marble goddesses, each
named for a northern city—Arras, Lille,
Rouen—louring down at me.

We know it well, know each corbel,
key- and corner-stone, as if by heart.
You are consumed, as always, by the
wild parade of the living, the aubergine
women, armed with batons and walkie-
talkies, stalking the parked cars,
the skate-boarding transvestites yakking
on mobiles, the louche boys patrolling
the tables, on the look-out for gormless
tourists. The ragged, the maimed,
the pigeons.

Thinking of all that, and of the sand
swirling round our toes in the Tuileries,
of the sweet (caramel, biscuit) and
salty (stale piss) smells of summer metros,
I conclude that if I were ever to glide up,
without you, from the underworld of
northern trains into the dazzling light
of a hot, dusty Paris, order a rosé
at the Terminus Nord and look across
at the railway basilica—

the hellish white of the portal would
tear the sight from my eyes, the bald-eyed
furies balancing on their pedestals would
swoop and strike me with axe, sword
and knife, passing boys would rob me
and I would stumble away to wander
the streets of Paris as once I wandered
alone among peacocks in a paradisial
New Delhi garden, seeing nothing.

Do you really think I could look again
at these end-of-the-line pillars and porticoes,
these blind granite women, remembering you,
and not myself be turned to stone?

Mary Noonan

Gomera

Fighting a hangover, I hire a car
to get us to Garajonay, the laurel rainforest
at the top of the island. We twist,
in endless spirals, from the hibiscus
of the hotel's Eden, to the date palms
of the lower slopes and on, in corkscrew
motion, beyond the dusty cactus zone
to the clouds.

The corners of my eyes are sending
alarm signals about a road falling away
on either side to mist-snagged ravines,
and I think about the Lanzarote wine
we drank last night, with a yellow griffin
on its label. The higher we go, the more
the brume descends, so that I can barely
see the hairpin bends spinning out
before me.

The woods are dark and deep, the road zig-
zags through them. At last we stop to peer
down, through a cold haze, at the layered
terraces and stone walls of the Valle Gran Rey.
Is that where the giant lizards live? As if
in answer, a small blue chaffinch hops
onto the path before us, seems to want us
to follow.

You press on to the hikers' bodega,
where warming coffee waits, but I'm a
captive of the *pinzon azul*—I agree to go with
him, to be a small ball of blue clinging to the
spindly arms of mountain laurel and pine,
to lie in the musky damp and look up
at the flamboyant trees vaulting
above my head.

I want to hear the shepherds' echoing whistles
as they talk to each other across the valleys,
to drink my volcanic wine and pirouette,
with my yellow griffin and my giant lizard
on the floor of a laurisilva forest on the edge
of a white-bearded ravine, five thousand feet
above sea level.

Mary Noonan

Snorkel

I pull on my wetsuit, my flippers,
my goggles, and attach the snorkel,
then dive in from the rock.

I'm a metre above the seabed.
The stones and sea-anemones dazzle,
then I meet the pair of seahorses.

They are dancing through the water
as if on TV. I waggle my snorkel
to high-five them, then swim on.

A turtle veers to intercept me,
flaps his flippers to stay stationary,
while he gives me a good gawk.

I leave him, and dodge a submerged
rock, on which a crab is sitting,
waving his pincers. Stay there,

I urge him, as two eels close in,
passing on either side of me,
then doubling back, while a jellyfish

approaches me. I turn around,
but I feel the jellyfish is gaining,
then I see the wings of the giant ray

blotting out everything else,
so I rise to my feet and wade in,
throwing the snorkel back to them.

Matthew Sweeney

The Singer

The singer hires a boat
and sails out, then drops anchor
a hundred metres from the pier.

Then he gets to his feet,
holding a megaphone, and begins
singing a reggae song.

A toddler on the black beach
starts dancing, a dog howls,
three cats come to listen.

Someone shouts to him in German
to fuck off. He increases
the volume, till the whole village

is out dancing, including
Germans, who denounce the first
Neinsager, and sing along.

Sunbathers trickle down the hill
to see what's happening.
The artists come to investigate.

Then the singer switches off,
takes the boat out to sea,
and shortly disappears.

The crowd call after him
but he's gone. They drift back
to their quiet worlds.

Matthew Sweeney

The Story of Dahnash and Ma'aruf
Deirdre Gleeson

THE STORY MADE OF GLASS

Dahnash was dreaming.

In his dream, the city was white and blazing in the sun. The boys had crowded around him, their arms outstretched, their eyes beseeching, until it seemed in his dream, as if they had merged into one boy with many arms and heads and eyes. But Dahnash did not need one boy in his dream, he needed many boys. So he split them apart and he sent them to the north and to the east, to the south and to the west of the city, and he told them to spread the word.

The audience they summoned was crammed into the corners and side streets off the square. It felt good to be soaking up the heat from the crowd, which now seemed hotter to Dahnash than the heat from the sun.

He was ready. He raised his arms and the people were hushed. His boys sat in a semi-circle in front of him. The words were building in his chest and throat. The crowd leaned towards him, rapt.

But the words did not come.

Dahnash pushed his tongue against his teeth. Nothing. He tried again. Only a noisy breath. His audience was not restless yet, but he knew that it would come, and quickly.

When he opened his mouth for the third time, he could feel the vibration rumbling in his chest, and a sudden push from inside his body, up his throat; his tongue moving in a way that it never had before, and then… a hail of glass fragments spewed from his mouth. Glinting in the sunlight, flying fast, out from him, streaking over the small brown heads of the boys.

Dahnash was excited. Never before had his words flown so far or so fast.

The crowd began to scream, as the shards embedded themselves in cheeks, and necks, and arms. Their cries turned to shouts of rage, and they flung themselves towards him.

In his dream, the bloodied hands of the mob did not reach the body of Dahnash. Instead his boys rose as one from their kneeling position and turned to face the crowd. He watched as their tiny bodies vanished under the surge of his audience.

Dahnash made to shout aloud, but the glass came ever faster from his throat.

THE STORY FOR THE GOATS

Then he was awake.

The burrowing snores of the herders turned in his head. Their tent stank of feet and the stale air of a night shared with fifteen bodies. Beside him their sleeping forms seemed blurred in the grey dawn light—less real than the dreams of the city he had just left. His arms, stiff and cold, still reached in front of him for the dying boys.

His nights always seemed to circle the same story now, Dahnash thought, the story of the boy lying in an alleyway, killed for the coins that Dahnash had given him.

These mornings just after waking were the worst. These were the times, before the business of the day began, when the longing in him was greatest. Sometimes he did not know if the hunger he felt was for the boy to be living again, or was only for the stories and for the audience that he had lost. He clutched at his blanket and tried to calm himself. The rhythmic snores of the herders continued to call and answer to each other around the tent. These men may have taken him in, but even in sleep he would never belong here, he thought.

His body intruded now, making itself felt. The pains in his back, the gumminess of his lips, the urge to piss. He struggled up from the greasy cushions that he had slept on and limped out of the low tent.

The sun was rising, cracking itself on the sharp and broken teeth of the mountains behind him, and the camp was already stirring. He cowered over the fire, and drew his blanket tighter against the whip of the morning sand. The women heated goats' milk for the herders' breakfast. Then the animals would be driven onwards through the hills to look for pockets of scrub. Dahnash would help as always with the gathering of wood, and the fetching of water.

As he crouched at the morning fire, and sipped his tea, he considered it again. In the stories he used to tell, a dream was never just a dream—it was a portent, a signifier of things to come. Wives dreamed of returning husbands, weary from battle. Merchants dreamed of losing their great wealth. Young men dreamed of princesses, and of liberating djinn from dusty oil lamps.

He wondered if his dream was not merely a retelling of his past, but rather might have something to say of his future? Could not this vision be telling him that he must attend to the other boys who were living, and not only to the one boy who had died?

He would go. He would go back to the city and seek out those other boys. They would not blame their old master for what had happened. He would sit with them and they would drink tea together. Dahnash would be welcomed. He would once again be beloved. And now as the desert wind began to blow especially bitter around him, he imagined himself back in the city, telling a story to his boys. This was why he would go.

He could not go. He knew he could not go.

Later as he walked with the women to the well, he could see the flare of the white walls of the city. They would not be back this way for months. But the herders were selling, and today Dahnash could see the archway of the northern gate.

'Do not come back here,' his sister had hissed, as she had passed him a bundle of his clothes outside the city walls that night. 'No one wants you here anymore—not your stories, or your boys, or any of it. The next time their stones will not miss you.'

He had argued about the fairness of that. Not with her though. She had slipped away in the darkness. No, back then Dahnash could make his arguments and tell his story only to the goats. He thought sometimes that this was the only story that he had left in him anymore. A story worn thin from repetition. A story without embellishment, or cleverness, or joy.

This is the story that Dahnash told to the goats: 'There once was a storyteller who paid young boys to bring an audience to hear him. Among these boys was one who we shall call the Catastrophe. One day a man killed this boy in an alleyway for his money. The people in the city were angry. But they could not find the murderer. So they blamed the storyteller for causing the boy's death and they ran him out of the city.'

The goats would patiently chew as they listened to Dahnash. But as he told and retold it, Dahnash had begun to grow angry with the people of the city, and with the murderer. And yes, angry also with the boy that was the Catastrophe.

On the way back from the well, he carried the water pot awkwardly. The women stared at him as it tumbled from his straining fingers. He watched the precious liquid leak into the sand. He said to them, 'Today, I am upset.' But the herder women did not understand him. He did not use the words of their language.

After he had spilled the water in the shadow of the northern gate, Dahnash thought, I could walk through that gate, and I would be inside the city. They are not waiting for me inside the walls with sticks. I could go, and I could see.

As he entered through the gate, he looked left and right, expecting to be recognised and expelled. But no one came for him. He could smell chickens roasting, and hear the pop of cumin seeds in cooking pans. He could see the dyers working on the rooftops, their arms and shoulders stained flaming red and cobalt blue. The people walked by him with their jugs of honey, and their bales of cloth, tall ones and small ones, in rough tunics, and fine coats threaded with gold. He looked at the faces shadowed in windows, at the old men spitting from doorways. The familiar thrum of the streets warmed him.

He would head for the heart of the city—for the finest mosque in the region, and to the place where the great souk throbbed. Where, as evening fell, the oboe players with their covered baskets, and the fire-eaters, and the storytellers would gather. Where Dahnash used to speak. He closed his eyes and he could see it again in his mind.

As he began walking south towards the great souk, he thought that of all of them, he would most like to find Ahmad. He recalled how Ahmad would stretch his arms out, begging them to recognise the wonders they had just heard. How the crowds used to give generously. Ahmad was the first and the best of his boys. This was the one he would visit.

THE VARIOUS HISTORIES OF THE BOY AHMAD

'Cure your shyness!' one of the sellers in the spices souk shouted to him, waving arak tree root and camomile flowers. Tables piled with seeds and the desiccated rinds of lemons and limes lined the alley. From inside darkened rooms, moon-faced men beckoned to him, vowing relief from all calamities.

'A secret blend of 45 spices,' swore another man, grabbing his arm. Dahnash shook himself free from the man's grasp, but bumped against an upturned box heaped with grains of paradise and powdered myrrh. The stall-owner glared at him. Dahnash staggered down the steps of a narrow street to the left, and sagged against the wall. Perhaps he had walked too quickly without stopping, for he found now that his feet seemed heavy and that his breath was troubled.

He began to think how unlikely it was that he would still find Ahmad in the square. Ahmad would not be frozen in place like some character waiting to be brought back to life in one of the stories that he used to tell. No, Dahnash should go to the neighbourhood where the scribes worked—they were the readers and the writers of all the business of the city—there he would learn where he could find Ahmad.

The scribes and their customers huddled together in pairs in shaded spots around the neighbourhood square. None of them paid any heed to Dahnash.

'Do you know a man called Ahmad?' Dahnash said to an old man bending over a broom on the steps outside the bathhouse.

The old man stopped his sweeping and clutched the handle of his broom with spindly arms. 'What is the family name of this Ahmad?' he said. Dahnash shrugged.

'He studies the stars with a lens made of glass,' Dahnash said. 'He sells gold rings and bracelets. No-no! He trades silks and the finest spices from the East.'

The old man began to sweep again. 'I do not know any such person,' he muttered. His mouth had curled downwards, and with a speedy flick of his brush, he swept the debris from the steps towards the feet of Dahnash.

'Perhaps you know Blahmad and Khahmad?' Dahnash said, but the man only shrugged. 'Cassim down the street makes maps, he will know where these people can be found.'

'I do not know anyone by those names,' Cassim said. He was a precise and off-putting man, with narrow fingers and a fastidious air.

'They used to bring people to the square to hear the storyteller Dahnash.'

'Oh him?' Cassim said, 'He and those boys were always looking for a short cut. But it came to a bad end.' He shook his head.

Dahnash flushed. 'Do any of those boys live around here still?'

'There is one I think… by the name of Ma'aruf,' Cassim said.

Dahnash did not remember a boy with that name. Was he the one who had brought the five gold pieces from the silk merchant? Or the boy with the voice as loud as a bell?

He must head further south to the carpet-sellers to find this man Ma'aruf, but he decided not go through the great souk. He would go west, and south, then turn back into the sun again.

In the souk of the carpet sellers, the men stood in the street offering tea for the weary traveller and promising the most magnificent rugs that Dahnash was ever to see. They were hung from the highest points in the walls, and stacked in doorways. Each carpet told its own story—the tree of life in indigo and orange, arches of ivory leading to the eye of the lotus flower. Finally he came to the place where Cassim had said that the man Ma'aruf lived. Dahnash shivered and he wished for an instant that it was Ahmad in his fine house that he was visiting.

THE STORY OF THE POISONED SCRIBE

Ma'aruf was frowning at his reflection in the washing bowl when he heard the knock on the door.

'Kifah!' he shouted, 'I'm late already—please see who it is!'

The house was silent, except for another insistent tap. Ma'aruf dried his face and stomped across the courtyard to the door.

He squinted at the figure in the morning light. The old man was stooped, with dusty clothes, but his eyes stared into Ma'aruf's, looking for something. Ma'aruf stuck out his round belly. Let this beggar see who he was calling on. Then the old man said, 'It is I, Dahnash.'

Dahnash, Dahnash… Ma'aruf winced at the aging body, at the shabby tunic and sandals. This was not how he had imagined their meeting again.

'I used to tell stories and you…' the old man trailed off. He looked unsure of himself.

'Come in for a while,' Ma'aruf said. 'I cannot stay long though, I am expected at the carpet shop of my father-in-law.'

Dahnash followed Ma'aruf into the reception room, then stopped to stare at the blue mosaic floor and the turquoise flowering rugs. Impatiently Ma'aruf gestured for him to sit. But now Dahnash was running his fingers along the plaster carvings in the doorway, as if he had never seen such things before. It was only when Kifah arrived with tea and fruit that Dahnash stretched himself on the floor cushions across from Ma'aruf.

'So where have you been?' Ma'aruf said.

Dahnash tugged on the arm of his tunic. For an instant, Ma'aruf was a child again in that square staring up at Dahnash as he pulled at his sleeve, desperate for that moment when he would begin to speak.

Dahnash said, 'I have been travelling extensively, collecting stories for the brother of the Sultan. I went to the furthest corners of this blessed land, all for the pleasure of the Sultan's brother.' He waved a hand away from his body, as if to indicate great distances travelled in style. Dahnash opened his mouth to say more, but the words did not come. He put his hand against his throat.

'If it's money that you want…?' Ma'aruf heard himself say, as he twisted the rings on his finger back and forth.

'No, no! In fact it was Ahmad that I was looking for. Can you tell me where he lives?'

'I do not know anyone called Ahmad,' Ma'aruf said.

Dahnash stood, relieved. 'I thought that you were one of the boys who used to bring people to listen to my stories.'

Now Ma'aruf stood too. 'I am one of those boys.' He smacked his hand once against his chest. 'We used to come in the morning. You gave us money if we had brought enough people to you.'

'There was Ahmad, and Blahmad, and Khahmad, and… Thahmad.' As Dahnash counted them out on his fingers, he felt there was something not quite right about the list.

'Ahmad and Blahmad… then why not Ch'ahmad and Dahmad also?'

Dahnash leaned forward, hopeful.

'The families of Firuz and Maghuib have moved away. Kafur is dead now,' Ma'aruf said. 'Salih is in prison. Harun is a beggar. Who is to say what name you gave any of them on any morning, or any evening? Then there was me, Ma'aruf.' He stopped, waiting for the light of recognition in the other man's eyes. But nothing came.

'And of course there was Ajib,' Ma'aruf said, 'but it was only after you played your part in the death of Ajib that you ran off, isn't that right?'

'Yes,' Dahnash said, 'there was...' He could not say the name. The words withered in his throat. With each moment of silence he could see the disgust grow on Ma'aruf's face.

He could not say to Ma'aruf that he created stories about the boys every time that they met, shifting histories that swirled around each child, about loyal camels and lost gold. Or that he told these little stories in his head so that when the crowds came, he would not stand with dust in his mouth and no words. And Dahnash could not say that he did not remember one particular boy or another, because they all had drifted from his mind after that one boy died in the alleyway.

As each moment passed, he could feel the tightening grip in his chest, and the strangle in his breath. And he thought to himself, is this what it feels like to die?

But then suddenly and quietly—at that moment when he thought he could not endure any more—a sensation engulfed him that he had not felt in many years. The words were falling from his mouth, easily, dreamily, as his eyes fixed elsewhere.

This is what Dahnash said: 'A long, long time ago, I had a story in my head. A sprawl of a story. Too long to tell on a hot afternoon in the square. I asked a scribe to write it down for me. We used to meet in the night when his other work was done, and I would speak until his hand grew too sore to write. This story of mine was three hundred pages long and not yet finished, when the scribe died—may Allah sanctify his soul. And now I am close to death myself,' Dahnash coughed, and pointed to the teapot.

He rolled the glass back and forth between his fingers. Finally he said, 'The scribe was poisoned. He had been sleeping with his neighbour's wife, they said. The neighbour slipped into the scribe's house and put poison in his ink.'

Ma'aruf sighed with pleasure. He felt that old desire to slip again into the story. To wait for the next word, and then the next. There would be nothing else. For a mad moment, Ma'aruf wanted to give himself over to it again—wholly as he used to when he was a boy.

Dahnash continued: 'With every word that the scribe wrote, the reed drew the poison into its tip, and its stem, and then into his skin. Every drop of ink that fell on his fingers, every time he touched the written page, his body sucked more of the poison into him. They said that his tongue grew black, and his nails grew black, and at the very end, even his eyeballs grew black with the poison.'

'Awful,' Dahnash said, as he stuck out his tongue and widened his eyes, so that Ma'aruf could imagine the blackness of it all. He took another noisy sip of his tea.

A small voice uncurled itself in Ma'aruf's ear, and asked him if this could be true. If Dahnash had really known a man who was poisoned with ink. If he had truly gone travelling with the Sultan's caravan.

'May I have another of your fine apples?' Dahnash asked.

Ma'aruf passed the plate with grapes and figs and slices of yellow apple to Dahnash.

'Such an unusual thing, this death,' he said, 'I never heard of it.'

'It would be a great pity to put value only on that which you have heard already, don't you think?'

Dahnash hummed for a minute, an odd tuneless thing that pushed Ma'aruf further back into his cushions. Then he said, 'It was a shameful thing, to sleep with another man's wife. The husband was proud, and the scribe's own family were proud. Perhaps that is why the people did not speak of it.' Dahnash stared at Ma'aruf, challenging him to contradict this.

'Please continue with this history,' Ma'aruf said, blushing. 'Where is your manuscript now? Did the jealous husband take it?'

'No,' Dahnash said, 'even after they put the scribe in the ground, the rage of the husband was not spent. He swore to burn down the scribe's house. So I waited until after nightfall, and I climbed the wall of the scribe's garden. I stole into his writing room, my hands wrapped in cloth to protect them and I began my search. Dawn was breaking before I finally found the poisoned manuscript among his papers. I stuffed it in a bag, and lost myself in the city streets.'

Dahnash chewed on a fig and he thought for a bit.

'I divided the manuscript into three parts, and buried each one in a separate place,' he continued.

'Why would you do that?'

'It was easier to hide in smaller pieces,' Dahnash said, as he crammed another slice of yellow apple into his mouth.

'Why did you bury it at all?' Ma'aruf asked. He could not help it, he was being sucked into this crazy story. Surely, Dahnash would not be so brazen to come here if this tale was not true?

'Would you pour me another glass of your fine tea?' Dahnash said, 'My throat is dry.'

He was tired now, tired with this effort. But as he looked at the skeptical face of Ma'aruf, he reminded himself that the listener loved the story, and loved the man who told the story. What else had Dahnash now but the shards of a thousand memories, sharp and shining in the sun? What else could he do but continue?

'Why did I bury it?' Dahnash repeated. He closed his eyes. 'I thought I wanted it back. To have the story heard through Egypt and Syria and Persia. But the dead scribe was my friend.' His body sagged. 'Suddenly the story was nothing but stains on a page. What is a word, when there is a worm? What is a story when there is flesh, and death, and decay?' Dahnash clutched the cloth of his tunic.

'And now that I am nearing death myself,' he said, 'now I want this story to be found again. Perhaps even to finish it some day,' Dahnash nibbled at the last of the grapes. 'And that is why I came looking for my boys—to tell them this.'

He felt emptied of words, but it was not bad, this new thing that now sat between them in the room. He would visit Ma'aruf again the next day, and tell him more of the scribe and the beauty of his lover, or of the dangers that Dahnash had faced when he tried to bury the second part of the manuscript. Perhaps Ma'aruf would bring his wife, his friends to hear this story… perhaps he could go to other houses and tell other stories…

'So you want my help to find this buried manuscript?' Ma'aruf asked.

'Ahh—yes, perhaps,' Dahnash said.

'Believe,' Ma'aruf whispered to himself. He squeezed his eyes shut. He was expected at the shop, where truth was found only in the hard heart of each carpet knot and in the weight of coins in a man's purse. He felt a hot wash of sorrow over him. Dahnash in his exile, with his old man's body, was not the only one who had lost something since they last met.

Ma'aruf stood. 'Let us go this very morning and find your pages.'

'Perhaps we may talk again of this tomorrow?' Dahnash said, 'My journey here has tired me.'

But Ma'aruf was already lifting Dahnash up by the elbow. 'We should dig up the first part before the sun gets too high. Wait a moment.' Ma'aruf vanished from the room.

Dahnash leaned back against the wall. He thought about running from the house, but he knew that he would not be able to do that. He had embarked on something and he must finish it, or he would topple and fall. He must convolute, and entertain, and do the things he always used to do. If a wife with a thousand and one stories could prevent her husband from killing her, then Dahnash surely could do a lesser thing with a couple of tales of his own. If he did his telling well, Ma'aruf would not mind in the end.

Ma'aruf had already returned, clutching a shovel and a leather bag with provisions from his wife. He kissed Dahnash on both cheeks. 'Let there be no more delay!'

THE STORY OF THE BURNING WOMAN

The sun was climbing in the sky as they left the house.

'It is many years ago since I buried this story,' Dahnash pressed the tips of his fingers into his closed eyes. 'First we must go east towards the mountains.'

As they walked through the streets Ma'aruf talked.

'Do you remember that story you told about the master of disguise who forgot his own name? What about the one where the Sultan turns into a monkey to spy on his favourite wife?'

'Of course,' Dahnash nodded. His mind raced down the streets ahead of him, to the left and to the right, looking for a good place to bury a manuscript.

Finally, he stopped where the buildings were largest with spacious courtyards hidden behind high walls. He pointed to the highest wall on the street. Only the underside of the orange tiles edging the top was visible from where they stood. Small holes in a carved door offered glimpses of an empty garden and a large house, with shadowy windows.

'I had forgotten how high this is,' Dahnash said, 'perhaps we should return another day with a ladder?'

Ma'aruf shook his head. 'We will ring this bell by the door and explain ourselves,' he said. 'We'll promise the owner only a short interruption and we'll leave the place with the hole filled in, taking only the manuscript which is yours in any case. A little unorthodox to be sure, but nothing to be worried about.'

Dahnash grabbed Ma'aruf's wrist as it shot towards the bell.

'I buried this manuscript in the darkness,' Dahnash said, 'and there was nothing *orthodox* about my coming or going that night. If we tell the man of the house what we need now, then we must also explain how the manuscript came to be there.'

Ma'aruf pondered this. Then he pointed to the house beside them where the darker stones were gapped and crumbling. 'There is another way.'

Dahnash watched as Ma'aruf inched his way up the lower wall, puffing as he reached for every hand- and foothold. Finally he reached the top and risked a tentative wave. He dragged himself along the length of the lower roof. He knelt, then squatted and finally stood, clutching the orange tiles. There he stayed, pale and swaying.

'Shall I come and get you?' Dahnash said. He had dropped the leather bag and had already taken a step towards the wall when Ma'aruf spoke again. 'No, I was—I was just…'

'Just admiring the view,' Dahnash called up to him. 'Just thinking how you might stop and take some tea, no doubt! Have that tea. Compose an epic poem perhaps—we have time!'

Despite himself Ma'aruf laughed. Scrambling, he managed to pull himself onto the higher roof.

'It looks like no one's been here for a while!' Ma'aruf called, 'But it's a long way down…'

'Take your time,' Dahnash said. His back hurt from all of the standing. Ma'aruf swung his legs over the inside edge of the roof. His torso, then his head vanished and Dahnash heard a soft thump on the far side of the wall.

'Dahnash—come quickly!' Ma'aruf hissed from the open doorway, He was looking wildly up and down the street, his grinning face red and streaked with grime.

Dahnash tapped the fingers of one hand off the other, as Ma'aruf led him through the gate. His next story would need to be cunning enough to lead them safely away from this garden, or the only digging done would be for his own grave.

The courtyard was so much smaller than Dahnash had hoped, and overrun with grass and weeds. The trees were bushy with neglect. Shrivelled apples gave way underfoot as the men walked through the garden.

'How did you get in the last time?' Ma'aruf asked, as he took the shovel from Dahnash.

'The lady of the house had at one time given me a key.'

'Well, there's no one here now to give keys to anybody.'

'Not necessarily,' Dahnash whispered, 'there might be someone watching us…' He squinted at the top window, shadowy behind a carved wooden balcony, '… perhaps an old woman, invalided now, but once a great beauty. They say she waits for her nephews every week to bring water and provisions. She will not leave the house where she betrayed the trust of her one true love with another much less worthy…'

Ma'aruf looked up at the top window, which was slightly ajar. He said, 'Surely the nephews would clean the garden when they came…' But he shivered. 'Let us not delay—where did you bury the manuscript?'

Dahnash closed his eyes and said: 'It was the clearest night. The city had grown lazy with the heat. I waited until the moon hung high and small in the sky. Then I came to the courtyard.'

'With the key,' Ma'aruf said.

Dahnash nodded. 'It was a different garden then. The fruit seemed to glow in the moonlight. A wooden canopy stood to the left, with a cloth covering it, so that the lady of the house could sit in the sun. It was very beautiful, even at night.'

As Dahnash spoke these words, he could see the silver wash of the moon on the house and trees, and the grey sheen of the polished stone path. He could smell the mint and the jasmine in the garden, and the heavy scent of the orange and lemon trees. And in the midst of those smells, he thought he could detect the scent of the lady of the house. Could it not become true, by the saying of it and by the believing of it? Could it not become true that in the corner of this garden a manuscript was buried?

'It's coming back to you now,' Ma'aruf said, clapping his hands together, 'I can see it in your face.'

So Dahnash pointed to a corner and he walked to the oldest tree in the garden. It seemed to consist of the trunk of not one, but many trees coiled around each other, twining shapes like the blackened body of a woman trapped under its bark. Dahnash put his hands on the trunk for a moment and said, 'I have buried the manuscript here.'

Taking three steps away from the tree, he stuck his heel through the scrub into the soft earth. 'It is here. I am sure that it is here.'

Kifah and her father would not have listened to Dahnash, Ma'aruf thought, as he took the shovel in his hand. They would have closed their ears to him. But they, obsessed as they were with the warp and the weft of their rugs, would have missed out on this adventure. Already Ma'aruf's faith had been rewarded. Already he had shown his courage in climbing the wall. And now he would dig for the manuscript. Who knew what wonders, what magic lay in those pages?

Ma'aruf grasped the shovel in both hands and began to dig. There was great satisfaction at first, the blade cutting cleanly into the surface of the garden, revealing darker soil where there had been dusty green.

'Do you remember the boy Ajib at all?' Dahnash asked the digging man. He wondered if it was too early to ask.

'Of course I remember.' Ma'aruf's face had a calculating look. 'Why do you ask?'

'Well… what do you remember about him?'

'He was the cousin of Maguib and Ali. I remember he was skinny, but he was a very poor runner. One time he went to buy a bag of honeyed figs in the market. He lined us up one beside the other, and after we begged him enough, he gave each of us a single fig.'

'I remember after he died,' Ma'aruf said. He had stopped digging. 'For three days you did not come to the square. Firuz and I waited for you, but you did not come. Then on the fourth day, the sister of Firuz said that you were in the square again.'

Dahnash raised his palms towards Ma'aruf. 'We do not need to talk about this now—'

But Ma'aruf was agitated. There seemed to be little forgiveness in his tone. 'No, I wanted to tell you this. I went to the square.' He yanked the stopper from his jug and poured the remaining water over his head.

'And you were there. But you did not move when you spoke.' Ma'aruf no longer looked at Dahnash. 'Your tunic was dirty as if you had fallen down. You started one story, and then another. Not one story was finished by you on that day. Then the crowd began to shout at you and they began to throw things.'

Ma'aruf dragged the toe of his sandal back and forth across the ground. 'I took nuts from the sister of Firuz, from the bag that she had with her and I began to throw them also at you.' He dropped his head. 'Then you didn't come back. I thought that you saw me throwing the nuts and that's why you didn't come back to us. Because of what I did.' He looked now at Dahnash, waiting for him to speak, but the older man held his head in his hands, and he did not look at Ma'aruf.

Ma'aruf turned back to his shovel, and he began to dig again. He dug quickly, grunting as he heaved shovelfuls of earth out of the hole.

Dahnash remembered. The shock of the first apple against his body. Each story he had started on that day led only to an alley and to the name of a dead boy. He remembered the heaviness in his throat. The sudden awareness of himself, of his arms, of his tongue. The words slowing. The coldness of the square. The people standing before him with thin lips and folded arms.

Until the arms became unfolded and reached for things that could be thrown. They came in a swarm after that first apple—more fruit, and small stones used to weight the canvas on the stalls, even shards of broken pots. He did not wait for their breath on his neck or their fists on his body. He ran from the place where he had built palaces with a sweep of his arm, where he had stolen gemstones for them, and unlocked dungeons with his words.

A wave of blackness descended on him. But still Ma'aruf continued to dig.

The back and sleeves of Ma'aruf's tunic were stained with sweat and filth from the hole. He stopped for a moment and took a rasping breath.

'You're sure this is where you buried it? Not in the far corner over there, or…?' his arm flapped outwards, as if to encompass a multitude of other possible holes in many other gardens.

'I'm sure,' Dahnash said, forcing himself to stand, then pace.

'I remember the shape of this tree,' Dahnash said. 'I have told you that the woman of this house was once a great beauty, but I did not tell you the history of how she became a recluse.' He waited.

'No, you did not tell me this.'

'This woman's beauty was matched only by the jealousy of her husband. He burned her body and her hands,' Dahnash said, 'when he found that she had taken a lover. You did not hear of this at the time? The people in the souks talked of nothing else for weeks… surely your parents, or your uncles told you this story? Surely they talked about this foolish woman who risked everything for a penniless writer?'

He looked earnestly at Ma'aruf, as if expecting some glimmer of memory.

'No,' Ma'aruf sighed, 'I haven't heard of this woman either.'

'They said that he built a huge fire in this very garden and that he twisted the lover's stories tight as a club in his fist. When the flames burned at their highest, he told her that he would burn her in her own clothing unless she confessed. But still the wretch would not give him the name. So…' and Dahnash gasped for breath, clenching his own tunic as if he wished to fling it into the imaginary flames that roared in front of his face, '… so he held those burning stories to the hem of her dress, and he waited until the flames melted the skin on her arms, and her legs and her belly, until no man would ever covet her again. Only then did he put the flames out, and leave her to keep vigil at this window above us.' Dahnash sucked the breath back into him. 'But now, because of the honest work you have done here,' he extended his hand to Ma'aruf to help him out of the hole, 'only now do we know what really happened!'

'What is it that we know?' Ma'aruf asked, frowning. He stabbed the blade of the shovel into the soil.

'The husband must have seen me digging in the garden that night. When he retrieved the manuscript, he assumed his wife had taken a lover, who had left this as a gift for her.' Dahnash flopped to the ground, holding his head in his hands. 'It was my manuscript that burned this poor woman. And that is why the hole is empty!'

Ma'aruf's brow furrowed as he tried to order the questions in his mind. 'But—didn't you say before…?'

'Let us not dally here too long,' Dahnash interrupted, nodding towards the shadowy window on the top floor. 'They say that the restless spirit of the husband still haunts the garden, waiting for the woman's lover to return.'

'So where did you bury the second part of this great work of yours?' Ma'aruf said, as the carved door slammed behind them. He longed to shake Dahnash until his few remaining teeth rattled in his head.

'It is buried in an even more inconvenient spot,' Dahnash said. 'Shall we meet again another day to look for it?'

Ma'aruf considered this. He longed for the sweetened tea and the leafy refuge of his own garden. But then he thought about the face of Kifah, and the face of his father-in-law, as he returned with empty hands after several hours of work.

'No,' Ma'aruf said, with an edge in his voice, 'we shall not waste this day without retrieving at least some of this manuscript.' He set the shovel on one shoulder. 'Where did you bury the next part exactly?'

THE STORY OF THE DEVIL IN THE ROCKS

'We are going to a place outside the walls of the city,' Dahnash said, 'I will tell you more when we get there.' They walked in silence to the northern gate. Dahnash indicated a circle of rocks beyond the walls with wells of sand between them.

'It is here,' Dahnash said, pointing to a dark rock with a crooked line of white stone in it like the horn of an animal.

'Do not touch the devil's horn,' Dahnash snapped as Ma'aruf made to trace his fingers along the zig-zag of white. 'Do you not see the white marks in each of these stones? Have you not heard the curse of the devil in the rocks?'

'No, and I don't want to hear it either,' Ma'aruf said, frowning. 'I thought you said the second place was more inconvenient than the first?'

'It seemed so at the time, I suppose,' Dahnash sighed. He needed to do better than this. '… I was hurried, with still two pieces to bury, perhaps that is why I remember it so.'

Ma'aruf grunted. 'Before I start,' he said, 'are you sure that this is the exact spot?' There was no kindness in his tone, and Dahnash thought, I should've told him in the garden, or when he was smiling and swinging his legs on the top of the high wall. But there was only one thing that Dahnash could say now: 'I am sure—I took six steps from the rock with the horn of the devil in it.'

'And there are no stories of famous murderers, or thieves or seducers who would have taken it, as far as you are aware at this time?' Ma'aruf insisted.

The eyes of Dahnash looked to the left and right, but he had no alternative. 'There are no murderers or thieves or seducers who have taken this manuscript, as far as I am aware,' he said.

He made himself laugh, a thin reedy sound even to his own ears. 'But what are we, without the stories of the thieves and seducers?' he said. 'Without them what have we, but the weight of the sun bending our backs, and work to be done until the grey light at our ending?'

Ma'aruf did not reply. Perhaps he had not heard, for already he was turning the top layer of sand over the rocks that surrounded them. With each shovelful of earth that came out of the ground, Dahnash seemed to have less water in his mouth and less words in his mind that he could use. He rose from his perch on the rock and he began to pace.

Ma'aruf kept digging. With each cut of the shovel into the earth, the bitterness rose in him. Dahnash was a fool with his fanciful stories, but perhaps he was the greater fool for believing in them. The sweat dripped over his eyebrows. His fingers began to feel like the flesh was too big for his skin. He had been right to turn away from these childish things all those years ago. Back then, his faith in them had brought him only disappointments. And now it was no different. His back was sore, and his arms were sore, but some perversity kept him digging, and he vowed to punish Dahnash for this foolishness. So he widened the hole away from the mark that Dahnash had made between the rocks.

'I promised my wife to go to her father's carpet shop this morning,' Ma'aruf wiped his brow and leaned on his shovel. 'Because I did not go, he will need to work longer today.' He forced the shovel into the ground again and grunted, lifting more earth over his shoulder to the growing pile behind him.

'But I am honoured to help you find the last work of your friend, the scribe. What did you say that his name was again?'

'It doesn't matter,' Dahnash said.

'Oh but it does matter,' Ma'aruf said. 'My wife's name is Kifah, and her father's name is Harun. Talk to me about your friend the scribe as I dig, I would like to know more about his history—about his name, his family, and the street where he lived. As you tell me the details of the man's life, perhaps the memory of his famous murder will come back to me.'

Ma'aruf broadened out the hole, lifting the smaller rocks with his hand or with the leverage of the shovel, until it was wide enough and deep enough for him to lie in it. He continued to dig as Dahnash stuttered over the details of the dead scribe, giving him a name, a family, and situating him in a street far from the house of Ma'aruf. Still Ma'aruf gestured for Dahnash to continue. So he was forced to provide the details of how the scribe had learned to write, and why he had never married, until the day he began his ill-fated love affair with the wife of his neighbour. 'No stories,' Ma'aruf would say whenever Dahnash began to tell an interesting anecdote about the scribe. 'Just tell me the facts and details of his life.

'It is an honour to dig up the work of such an upstanding man. Of two such upstanding men,' he said, bowing to Dahnash. 'Although I am puzzled that I never heard of such an unusual murder as a poisoned inkwell. They still sometimes talk about the death of Ajib, not every day, or even every month. But sometimes when we see a boy who bosses his friends on the street, or when a child dies, we remember also the death of Ajib.'

Dahnash continued his pacing, round the hole that Ma'aruf was digging, until he feared he would fall into it.

'The sun is hot now, Ma'aruf,' he said, 'we should dig again tomorrow.'

Ma'aruf flung the shovel out of the hole, narrowly missing the legs of Dahnash. 'Enough of this now!' he shouted, 'admit there is no manuscript here! There never was.' He struggled out of the hole.

Dahnash was silent for a moment. He could not say, There is no manuscript. It would mean that the story had failed. There had to be another way. He closed his eyes. There was always another way. The start of something fluttered in him. He took a deep breath, swelling himself with the words he must say.

He extended his arm towards Ma'aruf and he screeched, 'You! I'm not telling you where the manuscript is buried. You only want it for yourself!'

'What?'

'You only want to take it from me!' Dahnash taunted, hopping from foot to foot.

'But you were the one who told me to dig here,' Ma'aruf said.

'No!' Dahnash pointed a finger at Ma'aruf. 'I was testing you. And now I see the greed in your eyes,' Dahnash said. 'My name is still remembered in this city, and you? You still love the gold—the fine rings on your fat fingers tell me this!' He made a play at grabbing at Ma'aruf's hand.

Ma'aruf pulled his arm back. 'You see?' Dahnash called. 'Even as a child you loved money. I saw that even then.'

'It was not like that at all!' Ma'aruf was screaming now in the face of Dahnash. 'It was Ajib who loved the gold, everybody knew that—even you knew that. He would count it out and lend it out, but he always got it back. He never gave but the smallest amount to his mother. It was Ajib!

'Even you, with your head gone soft from pirates and princesses, knew that! So you had him out in the morning, and in the evening, scouting the crowd for you. If there was someone who had sold cloth or spices, or someone from a wedding party, you would know about it, and he would run back and forth for you. You knew this! Everybody knew this!'

Oh yes. Dahnash did know. He remembered that now, remembered how Ajib would say that he did not want to listen to stories, he wanted to listen for the clink of coins in people's purses. How Dahnash had laughed at that one, before he sent him out to bring another old man to him, who only wanted to go home, but who was bullied into paying to listen to the great Dahnash.

Ma'aruf pulled Dahnash by the elbow back around the wall of the city, and through the archway of the northern gate.

THE STORIES OF AJIB, AND THE STORIES OF MA'ARUF

Ma'aruf was angry. With each step that he took through the city streets, he stoked that anger. He would bring him to the carpet shop, and fling him on the doorstep, so that Dahnash could see how his fooling had disrupted a business. But Ma'aruf thought of the skeptical face of his father-in-law and he decided against it.

He would bring Dahnash to the square where he used to speak. There Ma'aruf would gather the people and Dahnash would confess to them that he was a man with no morality—a trickster and a fraud. But Dahnash would only tell some threadbare story about the Sultan and his brother, and the people would laugh at him. They would laugh, and they would say 'Ma'aruf must also be an idiot to have a friend such as this.'

So he decided to go to another place, where Dahnash would be forced to admit what was real and what was not.

Dahnash was sweating. The heat of the city sat heavy on him now, and the winding streets seemed narrow and tortured. Beggars snapped at his ankles. Hawkers screeched at him from their stalls. Even the women on the streets seemed to glower and jostle him as they passed. The stench of cooking food was turning his stomach.

'Ma'aruf?' he called, But Ma'aruf did not want to hear.

Ma'aruf was bringing him to the great souk—or worse to the square. Dahnash tried to pull away from him, but Ma'aruf tightened his grip and kept his onward march. Then he veered off to the right, and suddenly they were there. In the alleyway where Ajib had died.

'Look at this place,' Ma'aruf said. He had let go his grip of Dahnash, and the old man slumped against the wall. 'This place is real. Something real happened here. Just as something real happened in the place where his mother buried Ajib.' He looked at Dahnash, waiting for him to say something. 'These are real places where real things happened. Don't you see the difference?'

But Dahnash was not thinking about the words that Ma'aruf had spoken. He had not been in this alley since Ajib had died. He hadn't wanted to. Couldn't. Now he felt overwhelmed by the fullness of the place—the tilt of the chalk-washed walls against his palms. The curve and spike of grey shadow down the alley. The arches closing over his head to stop the topple of buildings. Above him a narrow strip of sky, precious, tentative. He had told and retold this story to himself so many times that it had become reduced and bare. It had lacked the fullness of the place, and, of course, of the person, of Ajib. Dahnash was not sure that he could endure the fullness of the place.

Inevitably, he began to imagine the boy, the setting of the sun streaky red, and the cooling dusklight in the alley. The man following him, perhaps calling to him. Dahnash ran his fingers along the wall, what happened here? Did the boy struggle, did the thief always intend to kill him? Did they know each other? And the boy, did he think he could escape? Did he fight? Did he kick? Did he acquiesce? How did the fear claw at him? He would never know these things. They would spin ever outwards without stopping.

He would never know these things, but the origin of it and the ending of it were fixed. He had given Ajib the money, and Ajib had been killed for it. There was no story he could tell that could change that. The boy was dead. And Dahnash had a hand in it. But as he stood in this alley now, and as he ran his fingers along the wall, Dahnash realised that he had wasted twenty years telling and retelling himself a story that was not the right one. His story should've also been about Ajib.

Ma'aruf was waiting for Dahnash to answer him. But the old man was looking at the walls, the earth, the sky. Not even acknowledging Ma'aruf. Not seeing him. Ma'aruf felt a swell of anger in him. Dahnash had never seen him—his gaze had always been elsewhere.

Ma'aruf thrust the shovel at Dahnash. 'Dig!' he shouted, 'dig now as I have dug for you all day.'

Dahnash gaped at the proffered shovel.

'See how it feels to dig for something that is not there,' Ma'aruf said.

Dahnash looked again at Ma'aruf. He looked at his stubby feet in brown sandals and at the irregular weave of his red tunic. He looked at his short fingers with the bitten nails, at his small belly bulging through his clothes, at his round face and his thin beard. He looked at his long nose, and long eyelashes, and at his dark hair cut tightly on his head. At his eyes. There were no more stories he could tell in this alley to win over Ma'aruf.

'Where do you want me to dig?' Dahnash asked. The shovel felt heavy in his hands.

Ma'aruf indicated a spot beside them. He leaned back against the wall and folded his arms tightly across his chest.

Dahnash ran the tip of the shovel back and forth across the compressed earth in front of him. He positioned the blade and stepped onto the upper edge of it. Only the tip of the blade entered the ground. Huffing, he pushed away a small amount of soil. He went again, half scratching the dust and dirt away. Already his arms hurt, and his back hurt. He wiped the sweat from his eyes. Again he pushed down on the shovel, again with little effect.

Ma'aruf had closed his eyes. And Dahnash, although his body ached, continued to scrape at the surface of the earth. With each lunge that he made with the shovel, he looked again at Ma'aruf, who stood as if blind at the alley wall, his chin dropped to his chest.

And so Dahnash continued, scratching at the hard, dry earth in front of him until a tiny mound of soil reached his ankle, and until he could see yellow lights dancing in front of his eyes.

'Tell me a story, Ma'aruf,' Dahnash said. The breath wheezed out of him now, and he stopped for a minute, clinging to the shovel handle to keep himself upright.

Ma'aruf opened his eyes. 'You really have learned nothing today!' Spinning away from Dahnash, he lurched back down the alleyway. He must compose himself. He should hurry back to his wife and to his father-in-law.

Ma'aruf stumbled forward. His foot caught in the uneven earth beneath him. He sprawled to the ground, his vision clouded with tears.

He must rise. He knew he should get out of this alleyway, and return to his old life. Once he left this place, he knew he would never see Dahnash again. He would be free from his tales of poisoners and burning women. He would be left without his manuscripts and moonlit adventures. Instead he would endure the tightening twine of his obligations. Until some day he would be as old as Dahnash himself and he would run his own shop, and warn his own son against the foolishness of fairy tales… He knew he must rise.

Gently Dahnash helped Ma'aruf up. He wiped the dust from his cheeks and his beard, and he brushed the earth from his tunic. 'If you will not tell me a story, then tell me the details and the facts of your life as I dig.'

Dahnash tugged at Ma'aruf's sleeve. 'As you have listened to me, I must now listen to you.' He dropped his head a little to show his contrition. 'Now come.'

He took Ma'aruf by the arm and led him back to the pitiful pile of earth he had shovelled. As he began to dig again, Dahnash said, 'In the middle of the facts and details of your life, if you would like to tell me a story or two, then I would not mind that either.'

Ma'aruf closed his eyes. He did not want to speak. But the words were tripping, fizzing on his tongue.

This is what Ma'aruf said: 'My mother Reh dreamed of an enormous cedar tree for ten nights before the night that I was born…'

Fear Bréige

He got away from a field of barley in County Galway,
wood-bones wearing trousers and topcoat
and wide-brimmed hat, hung casually a few squally days
by a roadside, nothing occurring to him,
straw stuffed up his sleeve, a pair of black eye-patches

fastened across his rag-bag face. Labourers trucking back
to the city gave him a lift—paraded variously
around the building site as 'boss', 'commis chef', 'rare
tulip', 'night nurse'. Cue a spew of jokes
and uncouth guff, but whoever would harshly judge them

mightn't as quickly grudge them the standing room
cleaved under their lime-bleached boots,
the 'floats' of gargling concrete, the slobby wheelbarrows
lolloped over ramps, the screed work and shaky
gantries, the iron-welted paws and eye-scalding dust devils.

Fear bréige—'scarecrow', 'straw man', 'man
who is false'—finally accommodated behind the basement
window of an inner-city dive, became
the incurious curiosity, a pine board for spine, a transverse
slat his arms at full stretch, a green-tinsel hair mop

pinned under the hat, twigs of blackthorn his fingery jut.
Did he feel before the lads could the rumble
rising from the street, hear the new optimism, himself
a sounding board for economic boom?
No, he was entirely witless. Yet the boom came, rubbing

its hands, talking big, gathering force. Their
employer had a simple policy: just build an' be damned.
Payin' over the odds for materials anyways,
shake a leg, boys, shake a bloody leg. Windburn, sunburn,
frost and rain, they worked the hours he gave,

continues...

soon were coining. Could afford a posher place,
but the ingrained things held, touflish and hovel comforts.
Revelled on bleary Saturday nights—as galoots,
muck savages, hullabalooers; returned, spinning fictions
to fit the rags-and-wood man for a laugh.

It's how he earns his keep, they'd say, it's how he
minds the house. He wouldn't answer to that, or, if he did,
no one heard. Given a good kick sporadically
but couldn't take umbrage, and when the wrought-iron bath
grew cluttered with bean tins, beer cans, spud peel,

left-over T-bones, truce between them was a pretending
of blame on him. Slowly he gathered dust.
And they would dance rattling scaffolds of high-falutin hotels,
size up swing-a-cat mews, sort snag-riddled
apartments, guzzle their lunches in big galvanise boxes

whose walls were bare except for the cellotaped
and crinkling poses of Page 3 models, and whose exteriors
provoked a sideshow of scrawls of graffiti
daubed by local kids wiping their runny noses. Clear-outs,
dislocations, clutter of traffic countermanding

the hard-won communal thing forever at cross-purposes
with its own good intentions, its blundering fall down
humanity all messy and glorious in hard-knock
existence—none of that was their concern. Just doing me job,
they'd mumble to complainers, before moving

again, quick and rudimentary with shovel and barrow,
power tool, trowel, sandstone lorry. Some
could go through brick walls for a short cut, others played
live-wire tamers in deadly earnest, more knew
how to make a hammer talk, a saw sing a song, dull wood

turn marvellous. One grew deft as a surgeon
in the ways he could swing and swoop a mammoth crane
on meticulous traverse of the gapped skyline.
So the asphalt thoroughfares gleaming with cat's eyes
and whited demarcations whooshed into gear,

the peg-legged bridges spanned high and low, the ring roads
led onto ring roads, the thronged arcades
hoisted domes and unweary cupolas. Great constellations
of steel and glass across which sky and cloud
would abstractedly slide came to pass—sunlight's mill

and splintering a fierce bedazzlement. So the tall trees
let linger at the perimeter of each new venture
made a show of old-world maturity, though if you scanned
for a moment they might semblance only
stuntedness in face of the high-rise they were set against.

Most things went up pre-cast monolithic, the votes
of corrupt servants of the people commodified
and biddable—secret, cash-stuffed envelopes, deals done
that could slew a shopping centre away
from neighbourhoods it was intended to serve, green-field

outskirts hurriedly rezoned and sectioned grey and pink
and yellow on maps in atria of council
planning departments. It was rock and roll, entrepreneurs
the new stars whirling their helicopters
above the heads of the commoners, shimmer of 'virtual'

fortunes, golf-coursed coastal rights-of-way, African
oil wells, pitch and toss of the markets assuaged
by insider tradings, moneymen and government ministers
privately tickling each other, tumescence
of bankers' bonuses, tease and titillation of social columns

continues...

in Sunday newspapers. How many ways can you sin?
Just one: by getting caught. Beatific republic
of the poor made to pay and scarcely visible the multitude
of true movers and shakers tasting only
their own sweat, uncelebrated struggle, honest and tenacious

as the overlaid, unloved, still-breathing humus.
Gazing of a morning with no food for the kids and no Santa
coming, a mother might stand skeptical of fairy lights
studded against a girdered sky—*Merry Xmas*,
Yuletide Greetings above her in-hock-to-the-lenders rooftop.

Seductive mantras, spin doctorates, financial analysts
luring the gullible, our 'spire of light'
a prideful focus, tallest sculpture grandstanding on God's
grunged earth, frenetic gaiety of youth
milling and sad youth gone flopping to grief, casual antic

of hula hoops slung over the upraised arms
of Big Jim Larkin, down the corner pub a gun fired, a hole
burned in a drug pusher's heart. But would you
not feel disposed to slum in your Provencal summerhouse,
or breast the wavelets of goddess Shannon,

explore her Allen, Ree and Derg in your pleasure cruiser
if you were a powerful union leader, a big
company executive, or a tribunal judge goodly gracious
in long-winded deference to swindlers,
your retinue and argument of wizards conjuring a fortune

from the legal light show? Politicians skied
to a Rio conference on tropical rainforests, 'no women'
aboard the government jet, 'only wives',
and plaintive the head of our nation doesn't know
why all the cribbers and moaners won't go commit suicide.

Plush hotels two a penny now turning empty, houses
foundering—o rainy isle—in rivered hollows,
their pipes burst, veneers cracked, jambs and architraves
gone to rot, slipshod manufacture, exposure
of multitudes whistling for their supper the unavailing

warranties, while the quick and easy cover-all
cover-nothing of cliché plausibly hums the burst balloon
of the golden egg of the arse of the goose
fallen out of the bucket. No waylaying old ghosts, penury
and emptiness, shivering home to haunt the dream.

As for our red-neck heroes with dirt caked
under their nails, those laid off big boots—well, pundits say
it's the nature of casual labour to take what's
available, to stomp expendable and unnecessary away
when job's done, to keep an ear out for the boom

that might give them a start elsewhere. Diaspora again, our
favourite chatter word. While the very rich,
whose country is all countries and whose nation is none,
save themselves a cosy refuge, scurry after
their squirreled profits, trailing hard-done-bys and promises

to bounce back stronger than ever. But the fear bréige,
grown weary perhaps of doom and droning
pessimism, thumped and clumped his two wooden feet
up step by basement step, out the streets,
across the fields, over freshet rivers back to the ground

where he first saw the light of barley flowing. There the crows
flap about him undaunted as before, land
on his head and caw in raucous glory, heedless of his story
and unimpressed equally by the unvarying
shape, the one and only, he ever seems capable of throwing.

Patrick Deeley

Watertight

The 'plum pudding' model having failed us,
in 1909, Geiger and Marsden
launched positive particles into thin
gold leaf to navigate atomic space,

revealed nuclei as planets circled
by electron moons. Only one in eight
thousand of their ions bounced back, the state
of matter revealing itself devoid

of the solid we feel and think we see—
ourselves, organic planetary systems
in ceaseless revolution, bound

together by unknowable gravities.
And still we wonder why impassioned hymns
fall on deaf ears, and all slips through our hands.

Patrick FitzSymons

À la Descartes
Michael J. Farrell

Picture, if you will, a tree-lined avenue curving gracefully for half a mile, its destination a mustard-coloured mansion crumbling under the weight of lost elegance. It was the hazy hour before dusk, when the day had given its all and was relaxing. The one looking out at the water lilies and beyond at the hills was myself, Bartholomew.

A man came into view all attitude—I'm above average in the insight department and enjoy premonitions and other epistemological irregularities. The man was on foot. He was carrying a plastic shopping bag held cautiously clear of his body the way one might carry eggs.

An author, I have tried in my own small way to add lustre to the human condition. I started ambitiously with a tome called *God Knows* written in the first person. No one who read it ever admitted it. Then came the brainwave and I wrote *Here Below*. With sensational, if I may say so, results. People everywhere, getting the picture, wanted to save us from ourselves. Rot, a lot of it, but the rest had merit: do good, avoid evil, get back on the bicycle.

Having provoked the populace into divulging, I felt a responsibility. Writers can't walk away from the mess they make. The resulting correspondence was stupefying as crackpots and others shone new light on the planet. From Plato's cave to the Bermuda Triangle they tortured me. Neighbours described neighbours breaking all ten commandments. Old curses were invoked, druidic spells paraded, rugby football and Wall Street derivatives brought to bear. Then popped up that man with the shopping bag, one Mossy O'Toole, who wrote a fabulous letter about the late René Descartes, who, as everyone knows, was invited by Queen Christina to emigrate to Sweden from his native France where he was already an exceptional philosopher. You may have seen his picture: a bony face with the hint of a snarl and the shifty look of a fellow who trusted no one and with good reason.

The pope was on his case for what might be heresy at a time when heresy could provoke an unhappy death. A stay in Sweden seemed what the doctor ordered. But the Stockholm winter could be atrocious. Queen Christina, furthermore, was a fanatic and made him get up at five in the morning to talk philosophy. Descartes hated early mornings. In no time at all he caught pneumonia and died. That was in 1650. The Swedes, embarrassed, gave him a quick, quiet burial. The plot would thicken with the years.

One could argue ad nauseam whether it's cool for a man with tangled grey hairs growing out his ears to wear diamond earrings in the same ears. Mossy O'Toole, in short, was not a conventional man.

'We're the Anglo-Saxon O'Tooles,' he said at a certain stage. 'We're to be found near Blue Ball not far from Tullamore. I myself am the black sheep of the family,' he added with a hint of pride.

I, Bart, when not saving the world, am a confirmed bohemian. I'm not sure what this means but it seems to include a wide-ranging neglect of the social order. The mansion is a mess. Several Irish wolfhounds spread fleas from room to room. Rusty kettles, heaps of unwashed laundry and a yellow canoe are scattered across the drawing room. They have not been disturbed for a generation or more. The philosophy behind this inertia is to the effect that life is short and should be wasted only on essentials. I am tall and gaunt, by the way. If you wish to envisage me, envisage me as a cricket player dressed to play, something I have never actually done. I have cohabited for years with a willowy companion named Bella, an exotic person dressed in long draperies to the ground. Salt of the earth, apple of the eye, one soon exhausts the superlatives when she comes up for discussion. Like myself, she is bohemian. Thus, when a loud commotion came to the front door that evening, neither of us—although we had both seen the spectre approach—was in a hurry to respond. Bang, bang, the knocker went, while Bella doggedly read a book and I doggedly looked out at the lilies. On the other hand, we are all fascinated by interlopers and pining for surprises. While we are, for example, afraid of the grim reaper, we are equally afraid, when the occasion arises, to refuse to let the bastard in. So I let the bastard in.

'*Mon vieux*,' he said, something he would say a lot. '*Mon vieux*, where has traditional hospitality gone?' He didn't look at me, as if he took me for a hired servant, brushing past with the plastic bag ahead of him until he deposited it on a table. 'You must be?'

'Bartholomew.'

'Oh, well, that's different. I bring you Descartes.' He looked eccentric enough to butt heads with Descartes, something few do: in our day only a minority wrestles with the dreadful questions. He wore a bluish plaid suit, too big for him now, as if he had reached and then moved beyond that moment when human flesh begins to shrivel and disappear. Then the freckles across his face came into focus, miniscule blotches, each a separate imperfection. Those freckles were, furthermore, unevenly distributed, seventy percent, give or take, on one side and the remainder on the other.

Bella made broth. Dandelion broth, she claimed, added iron to the soul. I kindled a roaring fire while Mossy enjoyed a bath. There was a sense of occasion. As our guest talked, those freckles would move about his face, a universe of miniature moons and planets in their orbits.

'*Cogito, ergo sum*,' he intoned. 'You don't need Latin to know Descartes said a mouthful.' An evening breeze was blowing past the double doors from the orchard. The broth was laced with spices and the dregs of several tall bottles. The result was a mystical twilight reminiscent of the evening the ancient Greek discovered Eureka.

Descartes, so the story goes, found himself lapsing into the worst of all possible frames of mind: universal doubt. This had not been a problem since God knows when. Previously, when incredulity raised its head, litanies of saints joined forces with ancient pagans to make blind belief a *sine qua non*. Yet Descartes' demons demurred. Show us, they insisted. A whole world teetered, the only world we had at the time. And the trouble with doubts: when you give in to one, another pops up until they're everywhere. Soon the philosopher was wading in a cesspool of misgivings.

Still, he thought, if I'm thinking about it, whatever it is, I must at least be here.

'It was brilliant, *mon vieux*. Everything else fell into place.'

'How?' Bella wanted to know.

'How what?'

'How did everything fall into place?' This is the kind of poky question no one wants to be asked, but Bella had a poky mind. A wolf howled in the distance, adding atmosphere, probably the neighbours' dog.

'If I'm thinking, I must be here,' Mossy tried to explain. 'And if *I'm* here, so is everyone else.' Philosophically it was a limp old sausage, not one you could sink your teeth into. But the wily vagabond forged ahead. 'When a dead man leaves ideas like that festering all over Europe, *mon ami*, there will always be someone to drag his memory over the coals—or am I mixing too many metaphors? And is that mead, by the way, in the bottle?'

'Wine, *mon ami*.'

'I have nothing against wine.'

'It's made from the same dandelions as the broth,' she explained. 'Earth is winding down, old man, and the dandelion is your best bet. That and the roach are the obvious survivors in their respective categories. After humans have succumbed, it will be the cockroach drinking dandelion wine. Or vice versa.' This aging girl, a nun in her youth, had spent life wandering from ashram to kibbutz to Amazonian jungle collecting nonsense. She had a great capacity for hope. She could see, down the road, a better life than life with myself, though she was vague about the details. This, by the way, was not such a startling discovery: I, too, could see ahead a better life than life with myself.

*

As the long twilight headed for midnight, Mossy asked if he could pitch his tent somewhere. This was a metaphorical tent and we pitched it on a section of terracotta flooring in the scullery. His only *impedimenta*, he explained, were a toothbrush and a pair of jockey shorts.

There was, though, one other impediment. Few relics create as much curiosity as a human head. Even the average skull: what a life it had, from the yowls of childhood to the hullabaloo, year after year, of facilitating what eye saw and ear heard, coordinating our days. I had been led to believe that one of the great skulls was in a box in the bag now looking conspicuous on the scullery floor. I nudged it with my toe. Whatever was in there was inert. It was mysterious. The world was always waiting for one Holy Grail or another. And like the lottery, I always thought I had as good a shot at it as the next one.

'I'm a troubadour,' O'Toole said the following morning, 'with no place left to go.' Thus began further days and nights of claptrap as the three of us circled the skull.

'Here's what I'm telling you,' Mossy was drinking tea made from a tea bag from his trouser pocket, a well-used tea bag, he said, that never made weaker tea than the week before. The followers of Descartes, in any case, asked the Swedes for his body back. When they dug him up, the French ambassador asked for the great man's finger as a relic—on account of the part the finger played penning the Descartes opus. 'There is embedded in the human condition a hankering for relics,' Mossy went on, 'from Marilyn Monroe's underwear to Moroccan jugs. But body parts are priceless. Locks of hair or a tooth but especially foreskins. Western civilization contains a vast treasury of foreskins. You'll find them in bottles and boxes, couched in velvet or in leather purses or ornamental reliquaries.'

'Descartes?' I steered him back to the topic.

'Oh that. An attendant, seeing the ambassador take the finger, took the liberty of taking the skull. There was dancing in the streets, *mon vieux*, when Descartes returned to Paris. It was around the time of the French Revolution, so no one paid much attention to a missing head.'

Yet a head is a risky factor to overlook. A skull is not merely a skull. No one would suggest, for example, that John the Baptist's was just a head sitting on a platter; or, later, just a skull. Once one got beyond the anatomy one suspected another dimension. Such as being godfather, in Descartes' case, of the mind-body break-up.

Descartes' remains, it seems, rattled indiscriminately around Europe. Then a Swedish scientist, Berzelius by name, read in a newspaper that the philosopher's skull was for sale at a Stockholm auction. He bought it for thirty-seven French francs.

'That skull,' O'Toole declared, 'has been sitting for ages in the Musee de l'Homme in Paris.' The freckles were going berserk as he piled one *je ne sais quoi* on top of the next. There was a notorious highwayman in that basement, also long dead. There was the odour of death, he said. He described the bewildered and ugly, the hairy and bald, the royalty and mountebanks—it was, after all, the museum of man, with an occasional nod to women. They were all dead. All except Descartes, whose *cogito* kept him from resting in peace.

'There's only one problem,' O'Toole said, after a week. He and the companion and I were sitting on the veranda overlooking what was once the family valley, trees of every pedigree basking below us, a fox looking for something to kill, a tractor groaning up a hill. I was growing sick and tired of Mossy, sick and tired of Descartes. Everyone said the latter's *Discourse on Method* was a powerful piece of writing, but I had never met anyone who actually read it, including O'Toole. Adding insult to injury, Mossy had taken over the scullery. A gaudy carpet appeared first. Then came items of antique furniture. A bird cage with no bird. A microwave oven. Only when I saw paintings of my ancestors on the scullery walls did I realise he was stealing from me.

The problem, according to Mossy: Descartes had been lost and found so frequently, there were now, in addition to the Paris skull, four others.

'All of them Descartes?'

'Who's to say otherwise?'

It took a shameless rogue to insist the others were spurious and the genuine article lying on my table. But one further clue kept popping up: the philosopher's name was said anecdotally to be etched on the true skull. 'Is anything etched on your skull?' Bella asked.

This would seem the obvious moment for Mossy to pull his prize out of the bag. But that was not the kind of man he was. 'Think about it,' he stared at us confrontationally. 'Descartes is the one who first announced the separation of soul and body. Don't you see?'

There followed a pregnant pause. Late in that pregnant pause Bella eventually nodded, yes, that she saw. And so did I. Nodded, I mean. I don't know why. Embarrassed, probably, not to know what the hell he was talking about. This embarrassment is surely the reason slipshod scholarship thrives in the world: no one speaks up during the pregnant pause.

Consider. One couldn't travel far in the arena of ideas without running into the soul. It got credit for most of our little victories in the past. How it achieved all this was seldom spelled out in detail because history was full of pregnant pauses during which doubters failed to speak up. At a certain point, therefore, it was assumed we all knew what we were talking about.

That was only half the catastrophe. While the soul was spiritual and flighty, the body, a heap of gradually disintegrating molecules, was easier to nail down. It had, for example, hairs in its ears. How such a body and such a soul, apples and oranges if you will, could ever conjoin and get along together—that was one conundrum. How they could now drift apart, as Descartes suggested—that was a bigger conundrum.

I myself—don't forget—was on a mission, metaphorically speaking, to rearrange the furniture, to comb our collective hair, cover the embarrassing pimple, set the sun back straight in the sky. People now wanted safer cigarettes, cuter children, less dirt under the fingernails, more snow at the North Pole.

In such a climate of misgiving, all those skulls had a disconcerting effect. Second-hand heads, if you like, already the worse for wear. Sometimes there were a few teeth left. Often there was an opening where none was expected. No two were alike. And that was just on the outside. Each of the misplaced craniums was on a shelf somewhere, probably in a fancy box, brooding and waiting. With or without teeth. Definitely without the tongue, the eyeballs, the old familiars. No more hair. No more wax in the ears. No more ears. A finger once picked the nose. Spare a thought for the finger. Those bones once spat and winked, somewhere back along the road we came.

And another thing. Killing, once practised only by a few, was becoming the rage. One worried that a higher power, if there were still one, might grow tired of us. The intelligentsia was befuddled. Writers hovered in vain over their computers. Until my own *Here Below*, which had been translated into everything, reminded people that nearly everyone, given the opportunity, disapproves of killing and prefers instead to talk things over. For talking things over, though, one needs pros and cons. And, as my book pointed out, the great proponents of pros and cons were philosophers. Of whom there were, I added tartly, precious few nowadays. This caused an outcry. Until, amid all the shouting, someone mentioned Descartes, and before I knew it I was locking horns with the ineffable Mossy O'Toole.

'We'll be having trout for supper,' I said soon after, 'with asparagus and the devil knows what. While we still have the long twilights, we might as well take a look at whatever you have in the bag.' This little speech had a galvanising effect. He went for a long walk in the rain. I could see him far down in the valley making up his mind. The modern world, he was surely thinking, was an old horse, tired, walking through abandoned meadows in search of a quiet place to die.

Supper: imagine three old wrecks like us gathered around a plastic table in the solarium. Small talk seemed superfluous. 'We could try uplifting music on the machine,' Bella suggested, dressed top to bottom in Carrickmacross lace. 'Sibelius, anyone?'

O'Toole countered with the Clancy Brothers and Tommy Makem. Since he still had the skull, the trump card, Tommy Makem sang about the wild colonial boy and the jug of punch while we washed down the fish with dandelion wine. A moment came when none of us could think of anything further to delay the proceedings.

A robin was singing a warbly song outside as O'Toole opened the bag, a mere grocery bag once, now the focus of almost supernatural interest. The box, I could see, was made of ebony, black and shiny. The opening ceremony was surprisingly banal, no golden key or electronic whatnot. He just lifted the lid.

One would like to think, if the Grail is ever found, that it will be a sensational find creating fireworks on earth if not actually in heaven, orgy and ecstasy and bands playing. O'Toole's package was less demonstrative. 'Go ahead,' the breathless companion encouraged. Even the Clancy brothers had fallen silent. There were no celestial phenomena. The skull, as skulls go, looked reassuring, typical. A mild, patient skull. Mossy picked it up without fanfare, without even the customary rubber gloves, and set it on the table.

We raised our eyes from the head and looked at each other. What could Queen Christina have seen in him? What could she have wanted to know at five in the morning?

'Doesn't look a bit like him,' Bella said.

The mouth was gone. Gone all the things it ever said. Even if it never was Descartes', it was surely once a talking mouth. The philosopher used to have an aquiline nose. Gone now the way of all noses. The brow was furrowed right down to the bone. All that doubting must have done it.

His name was etched above the eye: Descartes.

That seemed to settle it.

Saluti

So many are dying
it's good to see Kevin's
bronze face and white moustache

presenting a picture
of rude elderly health
marrying our Janet

under a flame tree in
the grounds of Government House
on a day in summer.

I wouldn't care to be
his liver but who knows
it must be up to the task.

Get ready then to hear
a cracker speech, with poem
and reminiscences—

no shortage of words, all
even the ordinary
inflected, inflated

and given (for god's sake)
life! So yes, celebrate
the bastard. Salute him!

C.K. Stead

Look who's talking

In my copy he wrote 'Arohanui'
and signed it 'Hemi'. Days now

he's been in my head, the atua
knowing I want to write about him,

smoking roll-your-owns, wearing
trousers from St Vincent de Paul.

He tells me a world without angels
would be suburban. No, I tell him,

it's the angels are suburban.
We bicker until he walks away

to the river with that long-haired girl
to do whatever they do there.

When I tell him he's a hypocrite
'Look at you,' he says. 'Look who's talking.'

C.K. Stead

Poem for Tennessee Williams

'None of my essential personality problems are solved.
I have not found the sustained desirable lover.
No new convictions—
no new lamp-post on the dark road I am stumbling crazily along.
I think I grow steadily a little bit harder and emotionally tougher—
not what I want.'

Tennessee Williams, New Orleans, October 29th 1941

All year you've stung with the failure
of your first play—the critics' howl
that it was *Amateurish, Repugnant;*
the Censor called in
to investigate its *putrid* lines.

Your mother echoes disappointment,
she finds your *work ugly, indecent*
and *a disgrace to her kinfolk.* Wary of offending
her Southern manners, your letters home
omit the truth of your days.

I don't believe anyone ever suspects
how completely unsure I am
of my work and myself.

On the other side of the world, war.
The theatres demand patriotic entertainment.
From a friend you borrow a typewriter
and put it in hock for a meal ticket.
Your weak eye needs a cataract operation,

an impacted tooth must be pulled, but not yet,
for now you must cultivate friends
who give dinners, live on fifty dollars
a month, accept *the squalor, the awkwardness*
and indignity of being broke.

What we need is writing
that gets at the fundamental falsehoods
and stupidities that makes the world
such a nightmare for most of its people.

Through practice you have become
horribly expert in the administration
of palliative drugs—
amusements, indulgences,
little temporary evasions and escapes.

On Royal Street you room opposite
the St James, from the balcony you
*hover like a bright angel over the troubled
waters of homosociety.* Only true friends
know how you spend your nights.

*I am moving. A misunderstanding
about some sailors who come in occasionally
to discuss literature with me
provoked a tedious little quarrel
with the landlady—I told her
I could not live in such an atmosphere
of unwarranted suspicion.*

December. The Japanese have bombed
Pearl Harbour. You are borrowing
against your gabardine suit. You wish
for a simple life with *epic fornications*
and make a religion of endurance.

Shore patrols and M.P.s raid the gay bars,
the life is going out of New Orleans.
But tonight there's a party
in the Vieux Carré.
While you are out

I aim to slip into the low light
of your dark days. I plan
to leave some bank notes
on your dresser. I want to thank you
for lines you are yet to write.

I want to tide you over.

Grace Wells

A Little Before Seven

Claire-Louise Bennett

I was cleaning out the fire grate, thinking a few things over, and as I tipped the pan vertical so the ashes dropped down into the bucket below I was struck by an observation that was as troubling as it was amusing: I can only withstand extended proximity to a man when I am drunk. Once acquainted with the observation I became immediately incredulous and somewhat sickened that this startling realisation hadn't hit me much sooner, since, it seemed to me, the instances upon which it derived foundation were not restricted to isolated and uncharacteristic phases, but more or less encompassed the entirety of my romantic career. At the same time, I had to concede that up until recent times I'd been more or less drunk a good part of the time—and, as such, had been routinely duped, in all probability, by a compelling but ultimately fallacious string of attractions—therefore, a revelatory breakthrough, such as the one I was presently undergoing, had hitherto been quite impossible. So strange and inevitable was this thought that I moved away from it for a while, then after a while, when I looked over at it, it seemed to me harmless enough, like one of those ephemeral epigrams one sees on kitsch postcards of housewives wearing high-waisted wide-legged pants in tropic shades of green. It doesn't mean anything, I thought, you're just going about a few tasks, amusing yourself as you go, don't give it another thought. Well that summation might be well and good—and its recommendation workable—if I had in any way changed my ways, but, in truth, the behaviour upon which the original observation was based more or less persists—and I could not, with good conscience, continue to turn away from it.

Weeks passed, however, before I took up with it again. Weeks, in fact, where I spent time with a man, sometimes in a state of inebriation, sometimes in a condition of sobriety, and, when I reflected upon this period of time, I had little option but to posit that, overall, relations with the man in question fared significantly better when I'd ingested a little alcohol. Clearly I could underplay the implications of this bolt from the blue no longer, and therefore took a little time, one particularly inclement afternoon, to ruminate upon it in a deliberate and dispassionate fashion—however, in truth, this methodical approach flattened my curiosity and stirred up nothing new to revive it. The observation just kept on repeating over in my mind like an appalling but dull diagnosis, and before very long I got up from my appointed seat next to the fire and went out the front to smoke a rolled cigarette and allow the many lovely things thereabouts to imbue upon my mind a more peaceable sequence of impressions. And then, just my luck, as I watched the branches of the beech trees being moved around by the wind, tossing out a few small birds here and there, an idea came to me with such sensational alacrity that it crackled with the showy insignia of spontaneous brilliance. However, the apparently impulsive manifestation by which this latest idea came to light was in fact not the least bit unprompted but was rather the sort of consolidated outcome which is typically produced when a protracted and half-hearted analytical process aggravates the superior auspices of an exasperated subconscious. Consequently, the emanation's illuminating glare softened soon enough, enabling me to continue looking at the trees while at the same time according the contents of this most recent development a privileged yet manageable place among my thoughts, and so it was that I was able to approach its meaning without panic or distress, when both or either would have been quite permissible—and thus calmly confronted the nauseating possibility that perhaps the reason why I'd drunk so much for so long was because I enjoyed extended proximity with men and since that closeness, which I so very much enjoyed, could not be brought about by any other means, I'd had no choice but to spend a good part of my time becoming drunk.

In many ways this aerated point of view appeared more troubling than the statement from which it had originated, and I was quite defeated in my efforts to distinguish anything amusing about it. In order to impart fully the seriousness of the situation I should make clear a distinction, and perhaps ought to have done so at some earlier juncture: I am not referring to the diffusion of those superficial inhibitions that may preclude one from being at ease with and enjoying the company of men in a recreational context. I have, in general, no inhibitions of this sort. In fact, from time to time, it has been pointed out to me, with varying degrees of justification and tact, that I'd do well to cultivate a little more social reticence, sober or drunk. Indeed, regardless of how aggrandising it all feels from the inside, alcohol does not reliably enhance the most charming aspect of one's public demeanour—so, to clarify—it is not mere confidence and conviviality that is sought during these vital sessions of artful libation, but the stimulation of a rather more sophisticated piece of kit. Something along the lines of curiosity perhaps—or no, the very opposite of curiosity in fact! A bespoke man-size filter for example, or a succession of perfectly pitched blindspots, or a discordant and enchanting ringing in the ears, or a swaggering crescendo of beatific bemusement. I don't know—whichever elusive device it is that surely one must naturally possess so that hawkish indifference is converted, rather niftily, into mindless fascination, and one's usual agitation has the opportunity to metamorphose into a gloriously abundant and terribly addictive suffering.

It might appear that this difficulty is merely circumstantial, relative to the second party in question, one that, as such, could be circumvented straightforwardly enough, were I to select to spend time with men who are in possession of qualities that are, in the most part, of an amenable and captivating nature. However, as tempting as it is to apportion responsibility, I'd be issuing an inadmissibly distorted overview of my encounters if I propounded the idea that, so far, I have not met with such men. I will not mislead myself or anyone else and pretend that I have not been acquainted with attentive, original and thrilling men. In fact, on the contrary, I have had the good luck to liaison with some of the oddest males the species has to offer. And yet, how to reconcile such a fortunate and encouraging record with the aforementioned assertion that I was, in the most part, quite unable to withstand extended proximity with any one of these extraordinary men until I had achieved a precise tone of inebriety?

Thoughts such as these lurched and abated throughout several afternoons of inclement weather and churning branches. In the mornings I did other things, and in the evenings perhaps I sat with a man and drank and got close to him, or didn't and became discomposed. On it goes. Essentially I cannot identify and fix upon an endurable purpose for them. That's what I've concluded and, in fact, from time to time, it has been pointed out to me, with varying degrees of infuriation and despair, that I'd do well to cultivate a more conventionally orientated set of needs. Which always comes as a bit of a blow it must be said, because, on occasion, I have gone quite out of my mind with love, and yet, as it turns out, that isn't quite the same thing. But, tell me, what else is one supposed to do? Get cosy? Get cosy, perhaps? Get cosy! They stand there, you see, these terrifying and familiar entities. They stand at the door, a little before seven, with a bag perhaps, containing god knows what. Some wine. Some flowers. Things like that. And I'll hear them coming. I'll hear the gravel, and when I hear the gravel I put myself in another room, the kitchen, the bathroom, sometimes, even, I'll put myself upstairs. I hear the gravel and the hook drop and the lower part of the door open and then, after a chasmic pause, footsteps, not many, over the stone floor. As this awful and accustomed entity makes its way in.

No, I'm not there. Never there to greet them when they arrive. What do they look at while they stand waiting and what thoughts pass through their mind? It is not immediately that they call out to me and I cannot help but feel that they are looking at something and often the feeling that they are looking at something becomes so abrading it erodes me and I tip-toe, lopsided, from out my subsiding hiding place. I come down the stairs or from out one of the adjacent rooms, always holding something, such as a towel. A towel, a newspaper I haven't been reading, a piece of laundry, a glass. Like something reclaimed from another world. But I don't stop. I pass through and vanish into another part of the house, as if the item I'm holding needs to be presented somewhere as a matter of sacred necessity. And they interpret this domestic fluttering as a cue, to move a little further in and set their bag of things upon a chair. I can hear them from the kitchen. I almost always end up in the kitchen, looking at the dishes and the knives on the plate rack, then down at the worktop, listening. Listening. In the kitchen, near the sink, some aspect of me is waning, and I cannot pinpoint exactly why. I feel utterly flimsy, yet I don't look in the mirror, nothing like that, I just stand for a moment with my back to the door and my tapering hands on the worktop, pressing down. Pressing down with the concentrated effort of trying to give myself a little more density. I go to the doorway. I go to the window. I go to the entrance and push closed the top half of the door. And then I move across to the fireplace, sometimes I put both hands flat against the oak beam, and then I turn, I finally turn.

But no, that is not it. I appear to have turned but I have only twisted—some of me has turned, and some of me has remained away. And yet it is an adequate gesture, enough to create a general impression of having turned fully and thus of being engaged and unopposed, even of enjoying the company perhaps. I do not have the courage to take the risk. To risk turning entirely and coming to face something very ordinary. I couldn't stand that so I stay twisted. And then I drink. I drink in order to—what?—become untwisted? Isn't that perfectly commonplace? Isn't that what's proverbially known as drinking to unwind? But no, that's not it. That's not it either. It's the location, actually—appearing to be located, to be precise—that's what I object to, and somehow wish to dispel. I want to shove the walls away and for the stone floor to turn to sand. I say such silly things indoors, the walls and floor and ceiling press so much nonsense out of me—I become defensive, critical, intractable and remote. Impossible! No, there are times when men and women don't belong inside rooms.

We'd be better off wrapped silently about each other next to a river or beneath the clouds or among the long grass—somewhere, anywhere, where something is moving. Isn't that right? Shouldn't we be somewhere where something is moving? It's the perfidious stillness I can't stand. When so much is at risk what sense can it make to be somewhere where apparently nothing is moving? There is music, of course, but selecting it is such a colossal anxiety—so often it comes out wrong and distorts things, like a poison, casting me in some dimensionless and highly-strung role, a perennially scorned revenant in fact. Preposterous really, yet barely surprising. They sit there, you see, biding their time. These awful and accustomed entities. Impervious, quite impervious anyhow, it seems, to the music, to the cupped hands and sipping breath, to the flocking shadows. Perfectly composed and biding their time. Awaiting that kiss which somehow settles everything. And I have to try, so very hard, not to say something imploring and juvenile, such as, I only wish you could just spend five minutes beneath my skin and feel what it's like. Feel the swarming vulturine magic I feel. But an invitation of this sort achieves nothing, worse than nothing: it comes to them as a threat. A threat they scrapple to keep at bay by tethering pathetic schemes of threadbare cosiness about the place. They move about your home depositing things here and there, making ordinary noises along the way, like it's perfectly acceptable. It's ridiculous and quite untenable to become enraged and put off by such gentle armaments as these, yet I cannot settle, and so I drink. I drink, to you. I drink, to me. I drink to love—I will not be let down.

A Little Before Seven

Walls

I smooth the blue walls
with an unsteady palm
pacing around the room.

I let your face come back to me,
our latticed fingers and tongues,
me curling your hair,
you stroking my cheeks.

Now some nights I embrace the quilt,
trace your countenance on the pillow,
stroke myself to recall our glory.

There are times when I want to
smash all the clocks in my house.

Then I think of you again,
a laughter that goes on,
a smile on a hard face,
a bare back at night breathing.

When we split I could not deny
that I mostly wanted sex. You left.
Only then my heart rose and like
an unwanted dog it chased after you.

Diarmuid Fitzgerald

Since 10 o'clock

At the counter I run my finger down my glass.
The cut lemon dries slowly, the pop song flickers.
The door opens with promise. You come in
and nudge near to me. We slip out and away.

In my shadowed room I smooth
a tongue-path to your nape,
follow your nose with my lips,
stroke your tense back as we curl and cry.

Now we lie in ease on stroked sheets.
Tomorrow you will be gone. Then I will
face the stale air, an unruffled bed,
one single towel on the rail.

Diarmuid Fitzgerald

Parchment

I do not kill the kid: this,
my only concession to a nice
squeamishness. The shambles knows me,
nonetheless, in the squealing dark
before dawn: I make my choice;
parting the springing hair to finger pelts
for ticks; the scabbings of disease.

A perfect, tender kid: I pay
without dissent the named price,
seize the rope, dragging her,
skittering on the filthy stones,
while I pick careful steps toward
the slaughterer, his precise knife.
It's quick—then all the rest is mine.

Sometimes, still, my stomach heaves
as I slide my blade under the skin
but more and more I hold a steel control;
release the hide and sling the carcase
into a sack for hounds. Then it starts—
the private ceremony: I am both priest
and silent acolyte, serving my end

in calculated patience. There is no miracle
in transcendence: no soft way. Prepare
for maggots, excrement and decay. Week
upon week ensue the unremitting rituals:
wash, scrape, scour. Day after day I stir
the clouded vat of slaked lime where the hide
haunts like a prayer; steep and drench again;

stretch it taut on the rack; abrade
with pumice in slow circles the refined skin
until it's done. Now, translucent to my lamp;
a bride, waiting for the event, it glows,
flawless. I rest, content at last to sleep.
No pride, I serve my purpose.
That is all.

Madeleine O'Callaghan

Golden Plover

My head is full of his yellow whistle.
He has been building a nest in my ears
For months. His call takes me to Cuilcagh
To watch him perform some ancient rite
Like a priest at benediction.

Golden flecked cape slung over his shoulders,
A white stole curves past the wings
Of his summer soutane. Flicker of bog-cotton,
Altar of votive candles, he raises
His black bill in a mountain whistle,

A heathery love call to his lady plover.
She sits on buff and brown-spotted eggs
In a love nest of sedge and moss,
Mother ground to old wisdom
At the edge of time.

When bog cotton turns to snow on stilts
The lone wanderers assemble.
Hungry ghosts, they scrape the bog for last seeds,
Flex their feet to dance under the Host of the moon,
Then fly away in strange formations.

Noel Monahan

Sense Memory Cares for Us Like a Mother

My friend said the skate, flayed, waiting
for the pan, its flesh had stung him;
arm trembling, he slid the fish into the oil
which soon made sweet the flesh,
made soft the bitter Amarone wine,
the bitter greens. Still stinging, he said
while I ate; I ate while mind
slid out the ray-like skate, slid in
a puppy-like ray that surfaced in its tank
at the aquarium—nodding up, and up
for my pat on its soft head: touch, a touch,
yes that is all, a tap a tap, on living skin.
That's how it is, you see, memory embracing
us as a mother would, watching out, taking care.

Diana Lueptow

Kindly Forget My Existence
Colin Barrett

Owen Doran was sitting at the bar of The Boatman Tavern when his friend and former bandmate Eli Cassidy came through the door. By then Doran was the Boatman's sole visible occupant; shortly prior to Eli's entrance, Doran had witnessed the Tavern's barman, a monosyllabic Eastern European with a pale, sharp-planed face, extravagantly scarred Adam's apple and skin coloured crewcut, step into a trapdoor in the floor of the bar. The barman, hitherto a clipped, evasive presence, had raised a brow, established one second of ferociously lucid eye contact and dropped noiselessly out of sight.

Consigned so abruptly to his own company, Doran had felt exposed, on display. To stem his self-consciousness, he'd futzed with the extremities of his suit—pinching plumb his shirt cuffs and tamping securely under his chin the swollen, inexpertly folded knot of his tie. He had nipped restrainedly at his beer and tried his best to ignore the ticking of the clock above the bar.

When the Boatman's door thrummed on its hinges, Doran turned to the source of the disturbance bearing an instinctive scowl; seeing that the intruder was Eli, his scowl deepened out of sheer surprise. But then it occurred to Doran why Eli was there. Wiping swiftly at his face with his fingers Doran permitted himself a corroborative glance at the bar clock—it was, finally, gone eleven, and it was a relief to know it was gone eleven. He turned back to Eli and modified his craggy, pug-dog lineaments into an expression someone who did not know Owen Doran might mistake for benign.

'Welcome, fellow coward,' he drawled.

Eli Cassidy blinked and frowned in his dark coat. A residue of the bright, rained-through morning had trailed him in and now it was diffusing from his hatless head and thin, sloping shoulders like a contagion.

'You on your own?' Eli said, shaking off his coat. Underneath, a black suit.

'The man will be back, he's just below ground a spell,' Doran announced. 'Drink?'

'Redundant question,' Eli replied, stalking forward.

Eli's rinsed brogues squeaked on the Tavern's floorboards. He transferred his overcoat from one arm to the other. Limply piled and dripping, it resembled the shapeless, lustreless corpse of a drowned animal. Eli heaped the coat on the stool adjacent to Doran's, but remained standing himself. Eli looked good, a trim man in his forties in a well-cut suit, though Doran could detect the ingrained reek of tobacco beneath the crisp ozone scent of his wetness. And the suit, on second look, was not quite pristine; there were streaks and gobbets of something slick adhering to the trouser legs.

'Is that shit on your knees?' Doran asked.

Eli looked down.

'Just mud.'

'Did you fall?'

'Yes,' Eli admitted. His face mottling, Eli considered the row of bar taps, their black levers level in the air. A little vein throbbed above his right eye. 'I'll just wait for the fucking guy, I guess then,' he sniffed.

Doran sighed, fitted his feet against the lowest rung of his stool and levered himself halfway over the bar, gut pressing into the counter's bevelled edge. He eyed the trapdoor in the floor, its rectangular metal door yawning upward, resting at a forty-five degree angle against a shelf of soft drinks and no sign at all of the barman.

With no little dexterity, Doran contorted his right arm in under the bar, extracted a pint glass, and from his side of the counter pressed down a tap and held the glass angled in place as he evenly poured a pint. Doran watched in the bar mirror as the glass filled, as the pint's head bubbled and bloomed. Pouring from the wrong side of the bar required the same queasy narrowness of concentration as writing with your weaker hand.

'Well done,' Eli said as Doran handed him the pint. 'The staff don't mind?'

'What staff?' Doran said, looking around and snapping two fivers from his wallet. 'There's one post, and it's been abandoned.' He put the money by the taps.

'How are you, anyway?' Eli said.

'How am I? A tad dismayed to find I've as little a pair of balls on me as you.'

Eli took a mouthful of his pint. 'Psychic of you to have the same notion, alright,' he said.

'Cravens think along the same lines. Though I was here first,' Doran said, 'which makes me definitively the cowardlier.'

'You didn't go up at all, then?' Eli asked, nodding towards the Tavern's windows.

Doran shook his head. His dirty red hair was gathered and cinched into a small, Samurai-ish pigtail at the crown of his head, and he had tidied up his beard, Eli noted. Doran was a short man with a barrel chest lapsing into a greedy boy's pot belly. He was wearing a cheap, boxy suit that was deep navy, not black, and his tie, unflatteringly wide and short, was patterned with what Eli now realised were tiny skulls. Such a flourish of gallows impudence was Doran's style alright.

'Did you?' Doran said. 'Go up?'

'I had a wander,' Eli admitted, low-voiced. 'The Cemetery first. To see where they were putting her. It's on a hill.'

'Maryanne,' Doran said.

Eli gave a small shake of his head. The shake was not demonstrative; it was to himself. 'Maryanne,' he said. 'When did you hear?'

'A couple of days back,' Doran said. He looked at Eli. 'I'm sorry,' he said, with a formal wince of his brow.

'Me too,' Eli said.

'How's Laura?' Doran asked.

'She's good.'

'She know you're here?'

Eli shrugged.

'And the baba?'

'I refrained from sharing my plans with the three year old,' Eli said. 'You got any creature on the scene yourself?'

Doran grinned. 'Those days are done, I'm almost sure.' He splayed a hand on the counter and inspected the digits, as if in a moment of recent inattention a ring might have somehow contrived to snag itself there. 'No,' he continued, 'I've entered the era of grand onanistic solitude, and to be honest, that's fucking fine by me.'

'I doubt that,' Eli said.

'Well,' Doran said, raising his brows and trailing diplomatically into silence.

Doran's eyes went again to the clock. Eleven minutes past eleven. The burial would follow at noon. He himself had arrived at the Tavern—which due to the steady custom of mourners maintained an early licence—just after nine, empty-stomached but full of cringingly honourable intentions. His plan had been to bolster his courage with a quantity of preliminary drinks before heading to the funeral. But the drink had not coaxed forth that kind of courage (as he knew, in his bones, it would not), and so Doran had sat, and not moved, and eleven had come and gone, and he had kept drinking in order to tolerate his ingrained cowardice. Cowards were cowards, Doran considered ruefully, but they required conviction to be so—the brave thing was usually the easier thing.

Doran took a long draught of his pint and smacked his lips with satisfaction.

'Mortality's a skull-fuck, isn't it?' he said.

'Hm,' Eli grunted.

'She wasn't well,' Doran said, 'is what I heard.'

'Me too,' Eli said.

'Did we always know she was not well?'

Eli considered the skulls on Doran's tie, the repeating rows of black eye sockets. He went to say something, but his throat refused, cracking and puckering inwards upon itself. He swallowed and began again.

'I don't know. You think on it, you turn things over. But the memories come out of your notions of them, what you thought was happening. And Christ knows we all had our dramatic days, back then. But if you're asking if I ever thought she'd do this.'

'It would never have occurred to me to ask,' Doran interjected, looking down into the sudsy, popping surface of his pint. 'Was it done violently, I wonder? Was there grisly theatre involved? A messy aftermath.'

'Christ, it hardly matters now,' Eli said.

'Or painlessly, hygienically,' Doran went on. 'There was a guy back in the day, and when I say day, I mean the forties. A writer. He done himself in and had to leave a note of course, had to attempt a pithy little addendum. "I am going to put myself to sleep for a bit longer than usual. Call it eternity," is how he signed off this planet.'

'You want to control it,' Eli said.

'Fuck her,' Doran said. 'Fuck her for what she did. And we're not even getting the worst of it, are we? We're the old guard. We're from the old way back days. We've already had to get over her, haven't we?'

'Fuck her,' Eli repeated softly, experimentally. He turned composedly to the bar. He kneaded the bridge of his nose, the sockets of his eyes.

'Sorry,' Doran said.

'Why? You're just Doran being Doran,' Eli explained.

'Sorry,' Doran said again, 'you know my cuntishness is as congenital as my cravenness. The only cure is no me.' Doran extended a beefy palm, patted Eli's shoulder. 'But I was always glad you and her got together, you know.'

Eli chortled. 'Now that was a bad idea.'

'It was a fucking terrible idea,' Doran grinned. 'But what wasn't, back then? After I quit I spent a season licking the windows in the mother's house in Portlaoise, for instance. You two tried, anyhow.'

'The marriage was insanity.'

'The glory days,' Doran said wistfully. 'You say we had our moments but not you. You were a good boy for so long. Sensible, abstemious. You were Eli, sorry, that sounds like an insult but it's not. Only she could turn you out of your equilibrium. She had a knack for it.'

'Not that she meant it, I don't think,' Eli mused. 'But she did make you want to lie down in the middle of traffic, alright.'

'Was that how it felt?' Doran asked.

'That's what it feels like it felt like,' Eli said. 'But I don't know. I don't know how it was for her. At all.'

Eli took a sip of his beer, Doran a deep quaff. The barman showed no sign of resurfacing; the clock ticked on. Eventually Doran gave a gentle, annunciatory clearing of his throat.

'She was our girl, a singer in our band, is what she was,' he said. He raised his glass and kept it aloft until Eli chinked it.

Eli could not deny that, at least. Sunken Figure was the band Eli, Doran, and a third friend, Proinsias Stanton, had founded in college, twenty years ago. Doran had been the original frontman and lyricist, ransacking undergrad poetry anthologies to flesh out the bloviated pornographic gibberish he half barked, half crooned. Eli wrote the actual music—clean post-punk lines and agitated percussion—and played bass. Stanton was lead guitar and for a time attempted to manage the band. Maryanne Watt first materialised on Stanton's arm, a serious girlfriend, in the long post-college epoch Sunken Figure spent toiling upon the capital's circuit. Stanton himself soon gave up, quitting the band for a job in the national forestry. Maryanne quit him and stuck with the band. Eli convinced Doran to let her on stage. And she did look good, rattling a tambourine and occasionally contributing tremulous backing vocals. Other members—drummers and auxiliary guitarists and keyboardists—came and went and Sunken Figure laboured amiably on, eking out enough of an existence to continually defer extinction, until the turn of the millennium, when something like actual success occurred. There was, finally, a major label deal, a hit single. There was coverage, attention, even money. And then came the grand folly; a marathon triple-figure-date pancontinental tour that ate up thirteen months of their lives and killed Sunken Figure stone dead.

The trouble started with the single. For the major's album, *Ley Lines*, Maryanne had sung lead on only one song, a B-side that was shifted up onto the official tracklisting at the last minute, but that song was the hit. Every interview and public appearance thereafter was an exercise in clarification. What the world wanted was more folk-pop gems smoulderingly essayed by the willowy brunette—instead it got more Doran, howling and spitting on his haunches over lengthy, bristling compositions. The classic soap-operatics kicked belatedly in: at some ill-advised point Doran and Maryanne began sleeping together. The tour just would not stop. As things soured Maryanne migrated from Doran's bed to Eli's. Eli had been sadly, silently in love with her since the time he had first laid eyes on her, and he gravely capitulated to what could only be a bad idea. Neither were the affairs successive, but concurrent. In the cramped, panoptic confinement of tour-life Maryanne alternated nights with Doran and Eli. Doran, surprisingly, was the one to quit first. With a month left on the tour, he stole away on a dawn flight from a frostbitten airport in Helsinki, made for the rural midlands town he had sprung from and summarily deposited himself into the care of his mother, to embrace what he would thereafter denominate his Brian Wilson Period; a six month interval of flannel-pyjama'd reclusiveness, weight gain, round the clock dope smoking and twilight bouts of compulsive weeping in the backyard greenhouse, the mildewed cord of his bathrobe stuffed into his mouth to stymie the worst of his guttural heaves.

Determined to salvage something from the implosion of Sunken Figure, Eli and

Maryanne got married and divorced fourteen months later. All through his music career, sensible and stoic Eli had barely drunk and studiously eschewed all harder substances, but by the end of their connubial stint Eli's appetite for illicit stimulants in general and cocaine in particular had outpaced even Maryanne's, no mean feat. What money did not go up their noses they fed into the production of Maryanne's solo record, *In the Gardens of the Lune*, a dauntingly ambitious, sonically incoherent concept album that took as its subject matter the posthumous travails of a fictional family of dead Jews (Holocaust victims, naturally) residing as superpowered ghosts inside the moon. Over layers of wintry distortion, painstakingly amateur-sounding instrumentation and time signatures so scrambled they practically induced nausea, the lyrics unpacked a labyrinthine downer of a narrative in which the family's little ghost son and ghost daughter commit ghostly incest, learn to manipulate the tidal patterns of the earth, and eventually cause the waters of the world to flood the entirety of Central Europe—all conveyed by Maryanne in an electronically treated, Bjorkesque fusillade of strangled yips, refrigerated keens and echolaliac blurts. The album was not well received.

After the marriage ended, Maryanne stayed on in London. Eli returned to Dublin. Doran, recovered from his fugue, showed up there too. Eventually the men crossed paths. There was awkwardness, but little animosity, and with Maryanne and Sunken Figure subtracted from the equation, they found making peace relatively easy. If they did not return, quite, to being friends, they were happy to let their orbits resistlessly overlap. Years passed. Eli became an accountant—he had a wife now, Laura, and a daughter. Incapable of any other life, Doran returned to the scene, scratching around with a couple of new bands, running DJ nights and picking up production gigs here and there. He became a sort of ironical eminence, courted by each new wave of local musicians ready to buy him a pint in exchange for a few war stories. But Doran seemed okay, to Eli, more or less functioning and more or less content, or contentedly discontent, and that was the best the likes of Doran was ever going to get. Meanwhile trickles of info regarding Maryanne made its way into Eli's ear. He heard she remarried, that she too had had a little girl. But nothing more substantive than those scant elementary updates, until this.

Doran said, 'I loved her too.'

'Yes,' Eli said.

He was looking at the windows. The rain had stopped. The inner panes of the windows were layered with dust; what light came through appeared microbial, quivering with impurities. The Boatman faced onto a lane that ran along one side of the cemetery wall. The cemetery gate was at the end of the lane. The procession, both men knew, would pass right by the pub. They would not be able to avoid seeing it, Eli realised, or at least making out its long, aggregated silhouette in those same dirty windows.

'I saw the family,' Eli declared.

'Oh?' Doran said.

'After I went up the hill I took a path down to the rear of the church. Curiosity, I guess. I hopped a fence and squinnied down behind a row of saplings. Hence the dirty knees. I hunkered down and watched through a bush, saw them going into the service.

'On your knees?'

'So I wouldn't be seen.'

'Ah,' Doran said.

'I caught a glimpse of them, alright,' Eli said.

Over the totality of the years, and even their marriage, Eli had met Maryanne's father exactly once—a tense hotel dinner through which Eli suffered the thin, vertiginous feeling that everyone at the table, including himself, was being played by actors. Maryanne's father, a retired barrister, was even then implausibly elderly, eighty-six to his daughter's twenty-eight, though he was still hale and snappishly alert. The woman accompanying the father—a dashing woman in her fifties with a sleek chrome beehive—was very much not Maryanne's mother. The actual mother was purportedly insane, certifiably so, and had been domiciled in an institution as far back as Maryanne could remember, and that's all Eli ever got out of her about her mother. There was one sibling, an older brother who worked in Futures, in Hong Kong, and who never came home.

'Furtivity is our natural state,' she had told Eli when he asked why she always said so little about her family.

'I saw the father,' Eli continued. 'Must be touching one hundred now. In a wheelchair, flunkies either side. Insane. I saw the brother. Had to be him, looks just like her. A double, disconcerting to see her in a man's face. I saw—I think—the husband, and the kid, her girl. But they didn't see me. And they wouldn't know who I was if they did.'

'But they would know of you,' Doran said.

'Maybe,' Eli said doubtfully. He drained his drink. He put the glass down. He blinked, heavy lidded. He was woozy after that single pint, and knew he would be on his ear if he went as far as three. He considered the door in the floor.

'He's down there? The guy,' he said. 'How long?'

Doran rubbed his chin. 'He must be in fucking China by now. Fuck this noise, this is negligence. You want another bev?'

Eli grimaced, considered his constitution, and said Yes.

'Hup,' Doran said, rising again over the counter and searching with his hand for more clean glasses.

'Eh, hi,' Doran heard Eli declare. Something moved in front of Doran. A package of refrigerated muscle encased his hand and commenced crushing his finger bones together. Doran looked up. The barman's smile loomed above him, mild and indicting, and beneath that smile a second one, lividly concertinaing his neck.

'No,' the barman hissed.

Doran wrenched his hand free of the man's pale grip.

'A word would've achieved the same,' he said, shaking his smarting hand in the air.

'Can't. Just. Take,' the barman said with infinite reasonableness. Then: 'What you want?'

Doran ordered the drinks and the barman picked out two clean glasses.

'What were you doing down there anyway?' Doran asked, nodding towards the door in the floor.

'Inventory.'

'Well now. That's as good an excuse as any. What's your name?'

'Dukic.'

'Do-kitsch?'

'Dukic.'

Eli watched the barman top up the pints and dip each in turn, tipping away the runoff. The sloughed foam pumped down the outside of each glass and sank into the grated metal recess under the taps. The barman was tall, six four at least. His scars were hideous, a row of ragged, mortified grooves bright against the lines of his collar.

'Well I'm Doran. And this is Eli.'

The barman gave an acknowledging grunt and distributed the pints, hooking away the empties in the same movement.

'This,' Doran said, and with his index finger circled his own Adam's apple. 'It's a nasty fucking razor burn, Do-kitsch. How'd you end up with it, if I may ask?'

The barman drew himself up. His lips twitched. He seemed to be deciding whether to say anything at all. Then he grinned, politely, as if he was obliged to find the reminiscence fond, 'I was in the war.'

'The war,' Eli said.

'Of course,' Doran said. 'And which one was that?'

'Bosnia. You recall?'

Doran waved a hand in the air. 'There was a bunch of them down that neck of the woods, wasn't there? Serbs, Croats, Sarajevans, all that noise, killing the shit out of each other.'

The barman nodded.

'I mean, it was complicated, so forgive my ignorance,' Doran said.

'It was not your problem,' the barman said.

'Though evidently, it was yours,' Doran said with some regret.

'Now just excuse,' the barman said and retreated deftly five feet down the bar. He stooped low, rummaged momentarily and returned to his full height brandishing a chequered blue and white terrycloth and a purple bottle of lemon cleaning spray. He turned a tap and ran the terrycloth beneath it, then twisted out the excess moisture. Onto the dark brown surface of the counter he dashed a succession of brisk, parallel jets of the lemon spray. He waited for the mist to settle before applying the damp terrycloth, bringing it in a neat rectangle around the sprayed section of the counter, then working inwards in diminishing, carefully concentric rectangles.

'Now continue,' he said.

'With the interrogation?' Doran smiled. 'Sorry. We just need our minds taken off the here and now. We're drowning in morbidity here. You get a lot like us, I imagine, funeral-goers in their maudlin moods.'

The barman, eyes following the terrycloth, shrugged his shoulders. His English was good, but it was impossible to know how much of Doran's talk the man was following. Without looking up he said, 'We get everybody.'

Doran gripped the lapels of his suit, flick-wrenched them into tautness. 'But not us, not us,' He singsonged. 'So you were in the Army then? In the war, in Bosnia?'

'Army. Yes. I was.'

'And that's when you got that collar?' Doran said.

The barman grunted again. He put away the cloth and spray, and travelled back up to the spigots, where Doran sat and Eli stood. To Eli, he said, 'Your friend talks a lot of questions.'

'That he does,' Eli said, wondering if Doran was going to keep at the guy, and already knowing the answer. Something like fatigue swept over Eli; as usual it would be his job to intercede, to referee or placate if Doran went too far with his escalating provocations, as he so often did.

'I'm just interested in the world. I'm an interested person,' Doran pleaded. 'You must forgive me in advance, like all my other friends,' and clapped Eli on the back.

The barman grinned again.

'It was friends did this,' he said, drawing his index finger across his neck.

'Friends?'

'Friends bombing friends. Our own men,' he raised a hand over his head and whirled it around, miming either falling ordnance or debris or both. 'Thinking we were not who we are.'

'Some friends,' Doran said. 'Jesus, huh?' He turned to Eli. 'Well, Do-kitsch is opening up now, though I couldn't prise two words out of him earlier.' He raised his glass to the barman. 'I'm sorry about your friends. But life goes on, huh? For us, at any rate.'

The barman smiled neutrally and tended to another task beneath the barline. Doran and Eli sipped their drinks. Eli looked to the windows again. It was becoming unbearable, the waiting. He felt a grainy runnel of dust in his throat and he could see, where the light was most acute, the motes scuffling in the bar's sealed atmosphere. He wanted air. He wanted a cigarette but he also wanted air.

'They'll be coming this way any minute now,' he groaned.

'Stay put. Keep the head down and stay put,' Doran said tightly, bolting what was left of his drink and whirling his finger for another.

'You are not going to your funeral?' the barman asked.

'Doesn't look like it,' Doran said.

'Why?'

'Ah, because we're scared,' Doran said.

'Scared,' the bar man repeated, huffing amusedly through his nostrils.

Doran shrugged. 'Look at us.'

'We're not,' Eli said, annoyed at Doran's insistence upon this point, even if it was true.

There was a lapse into silence, and Eli waited for Doran to fill the void. But it was the barman who spoke next. He extended a long finger towards Doran.

'Well, I tell you,' he said, 'you made me a little strange when you come in.'

'Me?' Doran practically squealed with delight.

'Yes.'

'Why?' Doran asked.

'I tell you,' the barman said. 'You see you look like a man, exactly like a man I saw in the street. In the city, in the siege,' he said.

Doran looked at Eli then turned back to the barman.

'Good fuck, go on,' he demanded.

'This man, he was trying to get to a woman and child. This is with the shooting, the bombs, every day, all day. Snipers in their holes, up high. Shooting all day. The noise of the bullets whizzing and whizzing in the air. The woman and child—maybe his wife, his daughter? They were already gone. In the street.' The barman held his hands vertically out, palms facing each other, then pressed them in close. 'In a thin? Alley. One and one.' Now his fingers pinched adjacent spots in the channel he had shaped in the air, placing the little bodies. 'And after a long quiet time, he come out, running. To get them, this man, you see. Crazy. Running, but too slow. The bullets, whizzing, whizzing. And so,' a jerk of the shoulder, 'he is one of them too.' He pinched a final spot in the air, like he was quenching a candle. 'He look like you.'

'He looked like me,' Doran cackled.

'Yes,' the barman exclaimed. 'This is why, when you come in…' he raised an index finger to his temple, corkscrewed it, 'and I am back. I am there.'

'He haunts you,' Doran said.

'Who?' the barman said.

'The man, the man, the man who looked like me?'

'Ah!' The barman hyphenated his brow in reproof of such a notion. 'Nonono,' he smiled, 'I had forgot him. Like this,' he snapped his fingers. 'But you walk in today, and so he comes to me. It was a long time ago.'

He put out two more drinks.

'A long time ago,' Doran mused in a smooth, declaratory tone, as if he was about to start telling his own story. But all he did was scratch at the stubble on his chin.

'Yes. Now please excuse, I must—' the barman forked two fingers in front of his lips and mimed exhaling, then pointed to the door.

'I'll join you,' Eli said.

'You're going out there?' Doran said.

'It will be fine,' the bar man said. 'Please, do not interfere again with the taps. I will be right back.'

Eli held the door. The bar man strode through, so tall he had to duck to avoid the lintel. Doran watched them go over the rim of his glass.

Outside the sky was a dismal monochrome. The men arranged themselves side by side on the lane's narrow pavement in front of the tavern. The cemetery wall ran tall. There were trees on the other side, their thickly leaved and shadowed branches jostling above the parapet. The barman was watching them. He had conjured already from somewhere a cigarette into his mouth. Unlit, he ignored it and stared fixedly ahead, his face in profile intent yet expressionless. In fact not a part of his body was moving; it was as if he had switched himself off. Such self-effacing stillness, Eli thought, must be a useful trait in a barman, who was after all only required to exist at specific intervals.

Eli nervously bumped a pack of cigarettes from his suit jacket. When he proffered a light the barman became abruptly animate again, turning to Eli with an appreciative grin. Eli lit them up, one and one. Wisps of smoke zipped away on a wind he could barely feel.

'I have a wife and child,' Eli announced.

'Yes,' the barman said tonelessly, as if this disclosure was to him a drearily familiar fact.

'Your story,' Eli went on. 'About the guy in the alley. His wife and kid. I have a wife and kid,' and felt instantly facile for having invoked the comparison.

The barman said nothing. He began to rock curtly to and fro on his heels, lending the impression he was shivering, although it was not unusually cold. He looked up the lane, down it, and then back at the trees; the smaller branches were in a state of continual minor agitation.

'It was a story,' the bar man said finally, with flat finality. 'Your friend made me remember.'

'Were you the one shooting?' Eli said.

The barman looked at Eli's eyes; not into, but at. Eli considered the possibility that this man deserved his scars—deserved worse, perhaps—but how would you ever know? Balanced against the doubt that his grievous little anecdote was either entirely fabricated or so extensively embellished as to be practically fiction was the doubt that it was not.

The barman took a dainty drag of his cigarette—he was smoking with such hallucinatory slowness that Eli was beset by the misimpression his cigarette had not diminished at all—and held the smouldering cylinder towards Eli.

'I thank you for the light,' he said.

'That's alright,' Eli muttered.

Eli looked up, and beyond the barman's shoulder he saw them coming. The long-bodied, shining black hearse, flanked and pursued by its trail of mourners, all moving together at a stately crawl. The procession came down the lane. Eli stepped into the doorway of the Tavern as the hearse went by.

Maryanne's father, a hairless, grim wisp in a suit and wheelchair was at the centre of the group in immediate train behind the hearse. A pouting kid in her late teens had been assigned chair-pushing duties. A stocky, foreign-looking woman was holding the old man's hand and leaning over him with a healthcare professional's solicitous disinterest as she paced carefully in step with the chair. Eli remembered the woman with the chrome beehive. She was evidently off the scene—she could be dead too, of course. There was the brother, paunchy, middle aged but retaining an indelible vestige of Maryanne in his face. There and gone, and after him came the husband; at least ten years older than Maryanne, a bushy browed man with a genteelly dissolute look to him, his cheeks rucked, a grey stripe running through his sandy hair, mid length and parted schoolboyishly in the middle. With his hands he was steering the shoulders of a little six- or seven-year-old girl. Eli knew who she was. Her face was mercifully veiled. None paid the least attention to the man dressed in black and the barman standing by the Boatman's entrance. The crowd's unanimous obliviousness filled Eli with relief, and made his laborious pre-emptive trepidation seem silly, for all this, he realised, had nothing to do with him.

When the last of the procession had passed, the door behind Eli opened. He felt something against his shoulderblade. It was Doran, grinding his forehead against Eli as zealously as a cat. Doran lifted his face, and turning around Eli saw that it was blotched.

'Ah fuck it,' Doran said. 'Let's do this.'

'You're coming?'

'I always was. But if I start bawling, it's 'cos I'm three quarters cut.'

Doran had brought his pint glass with him. He drained what was left and proffered the glass to the barman. The barman took it. Addressing Eli, he indicated with his smoking hand towards the receding procession.

'This is yours?'

'This is ours,' said Eli, dropping his cigarette onto the pavement and administering a summary stamp of his brogue as he stepped out into the lane. Doran followed. They soon caught up, and by the time the procession reached the cemetery entrance, the barman, still smoking and watching for nothing better to do, could barely distinguish the pair from the rest of the party, save for the substantial orange dot of the fat one's head.

The tall man and the fat man and the rest of the group passed through the gates and out of sight. The barman killed the cigarette and stowed the remainder in his pocket; no sense in wasting. When he went back inside he saw that the tall one had left his coat, lumped and dripping on a stool. It was a good coat, three quarter length and nicely tailored, expensive, the barman saw once he unheaped it and wrung it out. He checked the pockets for identification, but found nothing. He hung the coat on a rack in the staff room, scrolled up a couple of sections from an old Sunday paper, and stuffed the scrolls into each arm, dropping additional sheets of the paper on the floor beneath the coat to sop up any residual drippage, and waited for the man to return. An hour or so later a small band of mourners did drop in, but neither of the two men. The next morning the coat was still there, unclaimed. Soon, the barman thought, holding up another polished glass to the teeming, grained light that every day coursed through the Tavern's dirty front windows, the man will come back for it. But the man never did.

Fauverie (III)

You ask me to tell you what feeding time was like
so I start by saying how keyed up the big cats were, ready
to pounce on whatever the keepers thrust into their scoops—
the snow leopard shaking his turkey, the clouded leopards
tearing into white chickens, the black jaguar
gobbling his slab of beef. You nod
and say there is something you must tell me
but not yet, we have a meal to share, and once
you've told me your news everything will be spoilt.
The home help has prepared venison and an hors d'oeuvre
of foie gras, for dessert there's petits fours.
What happened next was that the snow leopard
wolfed down his turkey but seemed confused
with his rabbit, pacing back and forth
with it dangling from his jaws, blood trickling
down the long white ears. I show you the video
I took of his performance, my iPhone between us
as he yoyos from one side to the other. But I haven't
got this right because I filmed this twelve years
after your death, Papa, yet you are still chewing the last mouthful.
You lift the serviette to your lips and wipe them,
glancing at the clock above my head
as I replay the echoey voices inside the Fauverie,
one little girl crying 'oh le pauvre lapin!'
It's closing time and as the guard ushers me out
the lights are suddenly switched off.
I'm biting into my sixth petit four as you announce
'You no longer have a mother.' There's
the story to work out of how you know—
the phone call from my brother when he couldn't reach me at home
and had a hunch I'd be here, my secret three days alone
in Paris before I revealed my arrival.
There's a reel in my head of a leopard
who doesn't know what to do with the gift of a rabbit.
Every now and again he interrupts his circuit
and darts his face forward, startled,
then he's back into the loop, perhaps
needing to bury his bunny for later or
take it somewhere where no one can watch him eat.

Pascale Petit

My Mother's Salmon Skin Nightdress

With my pot of fish bladder glue
and my fishbone needle, my fish thread,
I am sewing my mother's nightie.
All my childhood I sew, mending it until bedtime
and each morning it's in tatters.
I mutter like a Siberian seamstress
as I scrape and soften new skins.
I study clouds to paint on her hem.
I came from the waters of her tummy to do this,
but each night she lies like a gutted fish
for Father the fishmonger. He strokes her
as if she's a salmon on a bed of ice
that should be dead but is still twitching.

Pascale Petit

Doppelganger

In Clew Bay's shallows chewed-up lumps of islands loiter
with one-storey dwellings clinging to their deformed edges
like adolescents on street corners, not one thing is regular
and I won't ask who lives here or who in this wasteland cares.
The tide is so high that it's impossible to walk out
without wading waist-deep in the detritus of this
absolutely small-time coastline but not far enough in
to refloat a flat-lining boat. It's abandoned face-down
at the shoreline, left there, like me stranded in this ugly
mud and sand land that can only dream of pasture.
Oh it's long past listing, that dingy is beached, bereft of any dignity
and I am strung out. Collie dog cocks his leg and pees on it
and I'm long past listening to those Brent geese getting
the hell out of here, the whirs and hoots of them escape me
because I'm exposed, I'm mainlining electricity from overhead wires.
Shhh, listen! They are singing-howling-whistling down
in my gut and out through the greyness of this autumn dusk
their twang could be from Siberia but on my hairline the wires
burn a thin cold bellow and I like it. I like the winsome Collie dog
and the streaks of sea-water rust on his white brisket, how it seeps
from his clammed-up collar buckle as he brings me the same piece
of sea-jaded timber over and over and over and I am on the air now
whinnying, I'm twanging like a string plucked and echoing,
here I am my own doppelganger. I am listening,
can you hear me listening and don't I sound just like myself?

Sarah Clancy

Black Vodka
by **Deborah Levy** (And Other Stories, 2013, £12)
Swimming Home
by **Deborah Levy** (Faber and Faber, 2012, £7.99)

In an online interview with *Granta* magazine, Deborah Levy reads a passage from her latest novel, *Swimming Home*. On the three occasions that she slips up, she does not simply correct herself and continue from there, as most of us surely would. Instead she returns to the beginning of the sentence or paragraph, proceeding slowly from the top, and it becomes clear to all that we are listening to a writer who places a poet's value on the rhythm of her prose. It asks to be read accordingly. To take just one example, from the title story of her new collection, *Black Vodka*, where the narrator says: 'I muttered something about being summoned to an emergency and left quickly before Tom could point out that the emergency was me.' Here we have a dialectically structured sentence, whose thesis ends extends to the word 'and', on which the line pivots before starting into its antithesis. The two sides, which each run to seventeen syllables, are sewn together by both repetition ('emergency'/ 'emergency') and rhyme ('emergency'/'me').

Deborah Levy has apparently been writing sentences this way since 1989, but her name was not widely known until she was shortlisted for the 2012 Booker Prize for *Swimming Home*, a short elliptical novel for which the sentence examined above could easily serve as epigraph. The novel opens on a Saturday afternoon in the south of France. Joe Jacobs, a famous poet, is sitting by the pool with his wife (Isabel), his daughter (Nina), and another couple (Mitchell, Laura) whom Isabel has invited. They notice a body floating near the deep end of the pool. Isabel dives in to help. When the body emerges safe and sound, they find that it does not belong to a bear, as they'd initially worried. Instead it belongs to Kitty Finch, the perfectly naked young woman whose 'breasts were surprisingly full and round for someone so thin.' Right from the beginning, we find Eros and Thanatos swimming in the same pool again. Kitty introduces herself and explains: 'I thought I was staying here from this Saturday for a fortnight. But the caretaker…' Isabel invites her to stay, and from there this novel of high symbolic charge bolts forth.

Kitty is by far the most interesting character in the book—a young woman onto whom everyone, even Kitty, projects an image. With the plurality of her narrative identity in mind, it should be said that her introduction to the group was not quite as easy as I may have suggested. 'What she actually said was I'm Kah Kah Kah and stammered on for ever until she got to Kitty Finch.' Although Kitty will go on to be extremely forthright with many of the other characters, she continues to spend a lot of time 'stammering and blushing'. As it turns out, she is a great admirer of Joe Jacob's poetry. She is something of a poet herself, in fact. It is from one of her poems, which she forces Joe to read, that the novel takes its title. 'The poem, 'Swimming Home', was mostly made up of etcs; he had counted seven of them in one half of the page alone. [...] He was being asked to make something of it and what he made of it was that every etc concealed something that could not be said.'

This narrative of silence and stammering is threaded into every line in *Swimming Home*, as the book, borrowing again from Kitty's poem, starts to fill up with its own 'etcs'. It all recalls the *Tropisms* (1938) of Nathalie Sarraute—another writer for whom there is no border between poetry and prose—whose characters are always 'jabbering half-expressed things, with a far-off look as though they were following inwardly some subtle, delicate sentiment that they seemed unable to convey.' When Sarraute was asked why she chose the word 'tropisms' as the title of her first collection, the nouveau romaniste replied that it 'came from the sciences, from biology, botany'. And so it seems quite appropriate that when Mitchell asks Kitty about her occupation, she replies: 'I'm a botanist.'

Sarraute is by no means the first proponent of the nouveau roman to whom Levy has been compared. In his introduction to *Swimming Home*, Tom McCarthy mentions Levy's name in relation to Alain Robbe-Grillet. Levy herself has drawn the same link elsewhere. In 1963, Robbe-Grillet wrote *Towards a New Novel*, a collection of essays in which he outlines the ideas and methods which he and other New Novelists had been working with since as early as Sarraute's *Tropisms*. Calling time on the nineteenth-century novel of Balzac and Zola, he argued that the novel must be newly conceived. His own fiction—of which *The Voyeur* and *Jealousy* stand out—was described by Roland Barthes as 'objective', a term Barthes elaborated on by reference to its dictionary definition: 'turned toward the object'.

It is a legend well-suited to *Swimming Home*, where Levy often seems intent on accumulating as many concrete nouns as possible just to see how they work together. 'Nina wasn't listening,' she writes. 'She had just seen a boy in silver shorts roller-skating down the esplanade with a bag of lemons tucked under his tanned arm.' In Levy's work, so much depends upon a bag of lemons. A still more striking (and literal) effort to set nouns together appears in 'Cave Girl', a story in *Black Vodka*, where the narrator states: 'There's been a pile-up on the motorway nearby. A furniture van collided with a baker's truck. The drivers crawled out of their vehicles streaked in blood to find a load of chocolate éclairs and cream cakes splattered on leather sofas and office chairs.'

Long before the success of *Swimming Home*, Levy told a 2004 interviewer that, 'what I don't want to happen to me is that thing that happens to so many women—it's as if we burst out of the birthday cake without context, history, or past with every book.' With some of its stories dating back as far as 2001, *Black Vodka* might be seen as Levy's attempt to contextualise her ascent from said birthday cake. It is an extremely strong collection, with each of its ten stories written in such high-concentrate prose as to reward not just several readings, but several *ways* of reading.

Black Vodka is an inexhaustible feast. Its richness can be ascribed in part to that style of weighted reticence we sense at work in *Swimming Home*. The recurring motifs and metaphors of the collection, which are each put down in such a way as to resist any singular interpretation, should also be considered instrumental. Levy records telephones, sirens and car alarms like others would record birdsong, while the grotesquely close attention she pays to wrists, thighs, skulls, bones, skin, meat, veins, blood and guts establishes an extremely rich, versatile symbolic code. *Black Vodka* sees Levy play surgeon, dermatologist and butcher all at once.

Above everything else, though, it is Levy's characters that make *Black Vodka* so densely elusive. Their world is one of pretense, performance. The narrator of 'Black Vodka' works in advertising, for example. He has a hump on his back, which he covers with loose-fitting designer suits. Similarly, he observes that his boss, Tom, who 'suffers from livid eczema on his wrists and hands', has always worn jackets with extra-long sleeves. 'For obvious reasons,' the narrator says, 'I am fascinated by how other people conceal their physical suffering.' In 'Cave Girl', the narrator's independently-minded sister, Cass, undergoes a sex change—not to become a man, but to become 'another kind of woman'. She returns from the operation with long legs, blonde hair and blue eyes, and performs as the kind of woman generally considered preferable by patriarchy. 'She doesn't have opinions; she listens to what I have to say as if I am someone important. And when I tell her a joke, she laughs, shining her dimples in my direction.' In 'Stardust Nation', Nick experiences traumatic memories of Tom's childhood. He is eventually hospitalised as he unwittingly performs as a sort of surrogate analysand. After Nick's recovery, Tom writes: 'For a man who had so recently been deranged he gave the impression of being entirely normal. I too have spent much of my life perfecting this performance.'

Levy has studied and worked in theatre, and so she knows as well as anybody that performances can often be extremely truthful. And yet it is hard to see how a cast of so many performers could ever be considered totally reliable. Since we can't quite trust them to be sincere—either with us or with themselves—we need to find other ways of understanding them. It is worth remembering now what Robbe-Grillet had to say about Barthes' interpretation of his work: 'When he uses the word "objective", he does not mean impartial or neutral. In a microscope, there are two lenses, one turned toward the eye and another turned toward the object.' In other words, Robbe-Grillet's extremely thorough descriptions of space are intended to reveal as much about his narrators as the space itself. As they delineate an object, the object delineates them.

One of the things that the characters in *Black Vodka* keep noticing is the distant cries of telephones, sirens and car alarms. These signs of alarm are made to reflect back onto their witnesses. In other words, they have a great deal less to do with anyone 'being summoned to an emergency' than with pointing out that, for many here, 'the emergency was me.' For Levy, what takes place on an exterior narrative level is absolutely tied up with the internal lives of her characters. Although they work slightly differently, rashes and scabs serve as still more exterior, objective manifestations of inner turmoil. 'He can live without champagne,' writes Levy, 'but he cannot live without his children; that is a grief he knows he cannot endure but he must endure and he knows his hands will itch for ever.' The fact that so many of the characters here suffer from persistent rashes (eczema, mostly) gives one further reason to suspect that, beneath the calm, measured delivery of its prose, the cast of *Black Vodka* are just barely keeping it together for the camera. The main attraction for us, then, is the suspense in knowing that at any minute the whole show might come down.

— KEVIN BREATHNACH

Shall We Gather at the River

by Peter Murphy (Faber and Faber, 2013, £12.99)

Spare a thought, if you will, for the failed messiahs, the prophets who came to nothing. We tend to remember only the relatively successful ones (Jesus of Nazareth, Muhammad, L. Ron Hubbard) or the more recent doomed claimants (David Koresh, Jim Jones, Marshall Applewhite) with their varying megalomaniacal tendencies. To test whether the latter truly failed we'd need to come back in several millennia and check if their ramblings had managed to take hold in a sufficient number of the populace. History moves in mysterious ways. What, then, of the others? Cyrus Teed with his teachings that the earth and sky exist inside a hollow planet under a mechanical sun. Arnold Potter who, believing he would ascend into heaven, leapt from a cliff to his death. The sleepwalking divine Jacobina Mentz Maurer. Mad John Thom the bullet-proof Cornishman. Tanchelm of Antwerp. Moses of Crete. Simon the Magus. Or the ones who might, in some obscure backwater, be subject to revelations right now?

In *Shall We Gather at the River*, Peter Murphy explores similar terrain to that of his largely-acclaimed debut *John the Revelator*. It's partially a tale of skewed adolescence (is there any other kind?) set in townland Ireland; a godforsaken and thus god-obsessed place. It's possible to label Murphy's style of writing as an Irish version of Southern Gothic with trace elements of noir and magic realism but to do so is crudely reductive. His town of Murn deserves to appear, on its own terms, on the maps of fictional places. For all the character sketches that make up the book, *Shall We Gather at the River* is on another level the study of a place where the transcendent and the macabre inhabit the apparently mundane, to those who are attuned to the right frequencies.

Central to the story is the Rua River, from which all the tales emanate and conclude. The title of *Shall We Gather at the River* comes from an old gospel spiritual from the nineteenth century, which in turn was inspired by a passage in the Book of Revelations alluding to a river of life flowing from heaven. Yet the Rua River is a cruel inversion of this hopeful idea. Murphy gives us succinct but memorable glimpses of the lives it will claim when it rises to flood. This river is nothing less than the collective unconscious with all its mysteries and danger, 'It knows where the bodies are buried, but will keep their secret, all their secrets, the whole town's secrets, the river air malarial with secrecy [...] And in their dreams the townsfolk do not speak. Because they do not wish to rouse the river.' This is the realm of Freud as much as Saint John the Divine.

The other main figure is Enoch O'Reilly, a well-defined but troubling protagonist. On a surface level, he's a difficult character to empathise with, which you sense is precisely the point. His is a mind pushed to extremities by the age and place in which he lives; the restless, ambitious mind grows deformed in such conditions. He lives during the Cold War; the great age of ennui and anxiety, when the West is affluent enough to induce mass terminal boredom but has developed the technology to deliver for the first time the imminent destruction of all humanity. Worse, he lives on a rock at the edge of the Atlantic. O'Reilly is a man for whom time is perilously finite and he is haunted by the frustration of being held back from life, 'somewhere a clock is ticking, ticking, ticking away his days.' 'Wary in his bones and in his balls,' he is nonetheless determined to 'leave this world like a fucking warrior monk.' For O'Reilly, the modern mythologies of radio and rock & roll are intertwined with ancient ones of place and faith. 'Elvis, Jerry Lee Lewis, Johnny Cash and Carl Perkins gathered around a piano in Sun Studios... the four horsemen of the rockabilly apocalypse.' The fire and brimstone preacher and the rock n' roll frontman are the only evangelising presences worth knowing. And both the pulpit and the radio lead back to the river.

The strengths of Murphy's writing are many, not least in skilfully avoiding the obvious pitfalls of his style. From the beginning, the descriptions of nature are hauntingly rendered, almost redolent of fairytale—though more *The Night of the Hunter* than Disney. Despite its shadowy subject matter, Murphy avoids 'murder of crows' clichés. His prose has momentum, an eye for intriguing surrealism and the unique poetry of local language. He frames parochial madness and those forgotten people, somewhere on the boundary between bathos and pathos, from the old men 'smelling of pub and wet dog' to the fellow who fires a shotgun 'into the ice [but] could not kill the river.' Occasionally the book is laugh out loud funny, often in demonstration of how the bored and lonesome mind turns to devilment, 'he hates the cabbagey, condensationed nights when there is nothing to do but stare at the ceiling and tug on your plum until sleep comes.' Having entered his father's forbidden room and usurped his 'holy ghost radio' (an echo of myths from Oedipus to the Salmon of Knowledge), Enoch resolves to become a priest. Thrown out of the priesthood for the problematic fact of not believing in God, he then seeks to become a preacher with catastrophic results.

Murphy manages to raise rather than dash narrative tension by revealing early on that many deaths will follow. The problem, however, arises in the arrangement of the book's chapters, which seems slightly rushed and disordered. Despite this, the scenes are richly descriptive and humanely characterised especially given their brevity. The countdown to the flood and how the corpses gather may drive the story along but the real substance of the book comes from brilliant but frustratingly-terse glances at deeper undercurrents. There's the central inscrutability of other people, 'not for the first time or the last, [he] ponders the mystery of the man who sired him.' This finds its expression most abruptly in the act of suicide, which Murphy ponders, 'Maybe a man slept too seldom and thought too much… Maybe a man numbed the pain with a little something, but that little something grew until it eclipsed the sun.'

For all its dark whimsy, *Shall We Gather at the River* is a deeply humane, funny, poetic and mortality-haunted book. It's highly readable (a grave sin in some quarters) and highly thoughtful (a sin in others). It's less an exploitation of the well-worn aesthetics of Revelations (after all the most emo as well as the most Bosch of the biblical texts) than a refutation of it. In a land where the holy ghost and damnation vie for attention with television and ego, Murphy masterfully conjures millenarianism, mythology, fraudulence and life-negation in small-town life. In these settings, the fear is not simply that the end of the world might occur but that it might not. And what strange, terrible, ludicrous lives we might lead, waiting to find out.

—DARRAN ANDERSON

Nice Weather

by Frederick Seidel (Faber and Faber, 2013, £14.99)

In his new collection *Nice Weather*, Frederick Seidel can sometimes sound whimsical and flippant; at other times, he is deadly and frighteningly serious. Seidel is a fascinating, infuriating and complex poet. His mordant wit is everywhere from the leap 'The Terrible Earthquake in Haiti' takes from its title to its first line—'I think the truth is I have to go to the dentist'—to the blank assertion that the 'usual liberal bs' is not something he cares much for.

The humour in Seidel's new collection is black and at times chilling. A persona poem 'In Midwinter', 'where Midwinter murder is in my heart' is not untypical:

> Patent leather makes my shoes
> Easter eggs by Fabergé.
> The shoes say New York is still run by the Jews,
> Who glitter when they walk, and aren't going away.

Seidel is a formalist; think Henri Coulette without the charm. He uses rhyme and strict, regular metre, but takes 'considerable pleasure in violating those norms' (*Paris Review*, Fall 2009). There's nothing 'New' about Seidel's formalism, other than the ironic, menacing and misleading patter to the iambic machinations of its lines. Born into a wealthy Jewish family in St. Louis in 1936, the poet shares his home town and Harvard as an alma mater with T.S. Eliot, whom he once met at the Faber offices in London and whose picture hangs in the poet's New York apartment. New York itself appears time and time again in Seidel's new collection. Central Park is a regular point of reference. In one poem the leaves on the trees in Central Park are popping and 'there's too much joy. There's no stopping. / Love's on top, fucking pain.'

Described once by the *New York Times Magazine* as the 'Laureate of the Louche', Seidel's loucheness is less appealing to some than others. *The Paris Review* has referred to his poems as 'disagreeable' and while writing about his considerable wealth, his penchants for expensive hotels, hand-made motorbikes, and sex with much younger women may have turned many off his work, he remains a poet to be reckoned with. When his first book, *Final Solutions*, was selected in 1962 by Louise Bogan, Stanley Kunitz and Robert Lowell for an award sponsored by the 92nd Street Y, the publisher and the Y rejected the manuscript because the 'matter in one of the poems libeled a noted living person', and, secondly, the poems were thought to be 'anti-Semitic and anti-Catholic', by the head of the YMHA/YWHA. The judges resigned and the collection was published the next year by Random House. The experience was a defining moment in Seidel's life and it was nearly eighteen years before his next book

Sunrise appeared, in 1980—this time to win the Lamont Poetry Award. Since then, Seidel has gone on to publish numerous collections including a *Collected Poems* from FSG in 2009 that gathers together half a century's worth of work. The longevity reminds you that Seidel was there when Ezra Pound was incarcerated in Saint Elizabeth's. In his *Paris Review* interview, Seidel says, 'I got Pound to recite poems by Arnaut Daniel and Guido Cavalcanti and Guido Guinizzelli. It was wonderful to see him tilt his head back and orate the poems in this very old-timey way. We got on very well.'

Although Seidel's Jewishness was not a barrier between the two poets, Pound's actual work was less of an influence than Lowell's, whom Seidel also befriended after interviewing him for, again, *The Paris Review*. With each book, Seidel began to outgrow Lowell's influence, and his work took on a more politically overt mantel. Now in *Nice Weather*, he writes with bravado about elections, presidencies, and even the environment: 'The shorebirds and the shellfish make merry in the giant oil spill'.

He tells us in one poem he is not happy with 'The President of the United States' and in another that the 'Republican and Democrats, [are] the nude / Alternatives to naked solitude.' Seidel is not adverse to tripping down memory lane either. In 'Back Then', he writes:

> Negroes walking the white streets
> Was how it seemed on Manhatten's Upper East Side.
> One morning in 1971 it began.
> I converted so to speak on the spot to the Ku Khlux Klan.

Seidel ends the poem by writing, 'I know the man who wrote this poem'. This ruthless scrutiny of the culture and the self's place within it is a recurring theme in his work. Seidel describes Montale's poems as 'a swaying rope ladder descending from some very high place', and his own poems sway under the formal and moral pressure he puts them under, even if, sometimes, the rhymes in his work are perfunctory and the matter occasional or self-pleasing. There's an insistence on how the poem struts and an obstinate assertion which often reinforces the 'beautiful pointlessness' of the pursuit. 'I don't believe in anything, I do believe in you,' he once wrote. In another poem, mischievously entitled 'Poems 1959-2009', Seidel writes, looking back at his life's work, that:

> You know the poems. It's an experience.
> The way Shylock is a Shakesperience.
> A Jew found frozen on the mountain at the how long summit,
> Immortally preserved singing to the dying planet from it.

Seidel's poems are performative, sardonic, scathing, brutish, arrogant and piercing. They can also be very funny. In 'Pretending to Translate Sappho', the undermining and rueful title gives way to the opening lines: 'The mother of the woman I currently / Like to spank, I'm not kidding, / Was my girlfriend at Harvard.'

Seidel once said he likes 'poems that are daggers that sing.' At other times, his ambition is as a more incendiary satirist. Take for example, the poem, 'Rainy Day Kaboom':

> Welcome to South Waziristan.
> I'm the Taliban.
> I wrote their poem 'My Poetry.'
> I meant it as an IED.
> O say can you see me driving over it up-armored.

In *Nice Weather*, Seidel remind us that 'the performance self opens the stage door':

> Sieg Heil!
> I said that to make you smile

and what makes Seidel such an interesting poet is that when you read his poems, it very often feel less like a stage door the poet or performance self opens and more like a trap door you, as the reader, are being pushed through by the entreating, graceful, but terrifying gentleman with the dagger.

—PAUL PERRY

121

SPRING 2013

Artful

by Ali Smith (Hamish Hamilton, 2012, £20)

Ali Smith is a Scottish writer best known for the daring and unconventional narrative style she employs in her fiction writing. She is the author of four short story collections and five novels, which have by and large been received with critical acclaim. She has been shortlisted for both the Man Booker Prize and the Orange Prize for Fiction twice, and her novel *The Accidental* was named the 2005 Whitbread Novel of the Year. Her most recent novel, *There But For The*, was longlisted for the Orange Prize in 2012. All this to say, that despite her playful and highly experimental narrative style, Ali Smith is taken very seriously as a writer of literary fiction.

Smith's latest offering, *Artful*, is a departure from her usual fiction writing. The book is created from four lectures that Smith gave to students at Oxford University, both traversing and illustrating the stylistic themes which form its chapters: 'On Time'; 'On Form'; 'On Edge'; and 'On Offer and On Reflection'. The book crosses genres; it is part literary criticism, part literature, part scholarship, part story. The narrator, a bereaved tree-surgeon/botanist, of indeterminate gender—perhaps a nod to the similarly gender-ambiguous, bereaved narrator of Jeanette Winterson's *Written on the Body*—is literally haunted by her dead partner, a former academic who was preparing a series of lectures on writing and literature just before her death. Smith writes a story about someone writing about writing in order to illustrate the elements of writing, which she writes about in the story. This sort of pleating and involuting of narrative threads, language and allusions, layer upon layer, is trademark Ali Smith.

Artful derives its inspiration from Italo Calvino's book, *Six Memos for the Next Millennium*. Composed of six lectures about writing and literature, which Calvino was to deliver at Harvard University, *Six Memos* devotes each of its chapters to exploring a literary theme or value: lightness; quickness; exactitude; visibility; multiplicity; and constituency. Calvino passed away before he had given the lectures and it was left to his widow to prepare them for publication. The parallels to *Artful*, both in form and in subject, are striking. In a passage from *Six Memos* that is quoted in *Artful*, Calvino writes:

> Think what it would be to have a work conceived from outside the self, a work that would let us escape the limited perspective of the individual ego, not only to enter into selves like our own but to give speech to that which has no language.

It is precisely this task that Smith has set herself in *Artful*. Employing a narration—informed by dozens of other narratives—within a narration, she attempts to escape the limitations of an 'individual ego' in order to 'give speech' to the elements of writing—form, time, edge, reflection and offer—which themselves are not written.

Smith's book is named for the Artful Dodger from *Oliver Twist*, and Dickens' novel serves as a thematic anchor for the stylistic romps of the book. The Artful Dodger speaks to Oliver in a strange language, a combination of a thick accent and unfamiliar vernacular, which Oliver has to decipher and which brings him to the realisation that words are much more than their literal meaning: 'It's as if the Dodger speaks another language altogether; and it's as if Oliver *has* to understand that a beak can be more than one thing, and a mill, and all the words that come in the paragraph after too, a stone jug, a magpie. Everything can be more than itself. Everything IS more than itself.'

The premise that everything is more than itself guides the study of the themes in Smith's book. The chapter 'On Time' considers the question of time through a multitude of parallel themes. Time is: death, aging, mortality, narrative, clocks, remembering, 'one thing after another', linearity and sequence. 'On Edge' yields reflections on: limit, possibility, experimentation, convention, the brink, extremes, liminal space, screens, borders and bridges. And so on. Each theme is explored through an avalanche of literary references and allusions in a ream of free association. Within a handful of pages we scuttle from the legend of Tír na nÓg to Walter

Benjamin to Joseph Conrad to Shakespeare to José Saramago to Katherine Mansfield to Michelangelo to Damien Hirst. And this is just a minute sample of the associations on offer. One is left with a dizzying series of impressions, the most enduring, perhaps, being that Ali Smith is remarkably well-read and prone to a touch of literary name-dropping. However, despite the barrage, the references are often pleasing, familiar and thought-provoking.

Ultimately, Smith's book is about imagination and the relationship between art and life. In this vein, she offers some pearls of reflection about style, literature, reading and writing and, furthermore, executes them skilfully through her own narrative. Musing on creation, she writes: 'It's the act of making it up, from the combination of what we've got and what we haven't, that makes the human, makes the art … possible, like it's the eye engaged in the creative act, in union with a kind of <u>not</u> seeing.' The blending of what is seen and not seen is a distinct and remarkable quality of Ali Smith's own writing style. Her use of language is daring yet masterful. Words and statements are left to stand for themselves, often in a play of associations where the gaps are as important as the connections. Consider this passage in which Smith describes the narrator's sorrow-cum-depression:

> Clever trees. Know-it-all trees. I was tired of tress. I looked up at the sky. It was there, like it always was, like it always would be. It was regardless. It had no eyes for anything but itself. Cut me open with a knife the colour of that January sky, take a sliver of sky as sharp as cheesewire and split me down the centre from here at the top of my head, and what would be inside?
>
> I went to the doctor and told him I needed help with mourning.

With Smith, things are often suggested, said sideways or sometimes not at all, leaving the reader to fill in the blanks, to grapple with what's there, but not there. It is, indeed, no accident that haunting, imagination and loss are central themes of the story within the story of Smith's book about writing.

About literature, she posits:

> Great books are adaptable; they alter with us as we alter in life, they renew themselves as we change and re-read them at different times in our lives … they allow for our mutability, are ready for us at all times … will hold us at all our different ages like it held all the people before us and will hold all the people after us, in an elasticity and with a generosity that allows for all our comings and goings.

The narrator's re-reading of *Oliver Twist* is illustrative. The same text, re-read, offers entirely new insights to support and inform a change in time, in circumstances and in life. Refracted through a different crystal—different eyes, different life—the text, as with all great books, will adapt.

Smith's own book invites a re-reading, too. Its density and its originality, its simultaneous playfulness and seriousness, mean that it cannot be read through and consumed satisfactorily just once. The book serves as a showcase of Smith's experimental style—playing with words, form and temporality—while excavating some of the aesthetic and literary influences that inform her work. Elements of the book seem autobiographical. It is tempting to read both central characters—the deceased and the bereaved—as voices of Smith herself and to imagine the setting of the book as her own home in Cambridge.

Artful will certainly be of interest to fans and readers of Ali Smith who wish to gain insight into her influences, sensibilities and sentiments—and it is certainly for this reason that I was drawn to the book. Furthermore, fiction writers, avid readers and students of literature should enjoy the fusing of literary musings with Smith's unique brand of fiction—although it must be acknowledged that the book's dense and sometimes academic style might challenge or vex some readers. However, as a work with many facets and entry points, there is surely something for everyone in *Artful*. Like the Artful Dodger himself, it is a work of possibility and plurality, and Smith—playing as always with her words—reminds us of that: 'I liked how when [Oliver] meets 'the Artful', the book really comes alive, almost because he begins to understand about colourful language, and I liked how Dickens called the Dodger all his names, the Artful, the Dodger, the Artful Dodger, Jack Dawkins, Mr John Dawkins, like he was a work of shifting possibility.' *Artful* is precisely that.

—LUNA DOLEZAL

NOTES ON CONTRIBUTORS

Darran Anderson is a writer from Derry. He co-edits *3:AM Magazine*. He has recently completed books on Jack Kerouac for Reaktion and Serge Gainsbourg's *Histoire de Melody Nelson* for Bloomsbury's 33 1/3 series. He is currently working on a new poetry collection called *The Fragmenting Man*.

Colin Barrett is from Mayo. In 2009 he received his MA in Creative Writing from UCD, and he was awarded an Arts Council bursary in 2010. Several of his stories have appeared in *The Stinging Fly*, and a first collection is forthcoming from Stinging Fly Press in September 2013. He has a story in *Town and Country*, the new anthology of Irish short stories edited by Kevin Barry (Faber and Faber, June 2013).

Claire-Louise Flitcroft Bennett was born in Barrow-in-Furness on Morecombe Bay and worked for many years below stairs all over Lancashire before she quite forgot herself and encouraged a retired foreign dignitary into an indoor game of leapfrog. His enjoyment notwithstanding, she was swiftly dispatched to Ireland where she keeps a small bird sanctuary and shuffles collectible saucers absentmindedly.

Kevin Breathnach is a recent graduate of Trinity College Dublin, where he studied French and Philosophy. His work has appeared in *The New Inquiry*, *3:AM Magazine*, *The Quarterly Conversation* and *Totally Dublin*. He currently lives in Munich, Germany.

Kimberly Campanello was born in Elkhart, Indiana, and now divides her time between Dublin and London. Her pamphlet, *Spinning Cities*, was published by Wurm Press in 2011, and her first full-length collection, *Consent*, will be published by Doire Press in Spring 2013. She was a featured poet in the Summer 2010 issue of *The Stinging Fly*.

Sarah Clancy has published two collections of poetry: *Stacey and the Mechanical Bull* from Lapwing in 2011 and *Thanks for Nothing, Hippies* from Salmon Poetry 2012. She has won or been shortlisted in both performance poetry slams and conventional poetry competitions. She collaborated with fellow Galway poet Elaine Feeney on *Cinderella Backwards*, a CD of poetry which was released earlier this year.

Michael G. Cronin is Lecturer in English at NUI Maynooth. His *Impure Thoughts: Sexuality, Catholicism and Literature in twentieth-century Ireland* is forthcoming from Manchester University Press.

Adam Crothers was born in Belfast in 1984 and lives in Cambridge, working at St John's College Library. A winner of the Quiller-Couch and Brewer Hall prizes, and the writer of *PN Review*'s 'Vestiges' feature, his poems have also appeared in *Ducts*, *Icarus*, *The Literateur* and *Poetry Proper*, among others.

Kevin Curran comes from Balbriggan, County Dublin. He has a Masters in Anglo-Irish Literature from UCD. He took part in the Stinging Fly Novel Writing Workshop with Sean O'Reilly and the Irish Writers' Centre's Novel Fair. His debut novel, *Beatsploitation*, will be released in May 2013 by Liberties Press. He will be appearing at the Belfast Book Festival in June.

Patrick Deeley is from Loughrea, County Galway. His poems have appeared widely in Ireland and abroad over the last thirty years. His six collections include *The Bones of Creation*, *Decoding Samara* and *Names for Love*. *Groundswell: New and Selected Poems* will be published by Dedalus Press this April.

Deirdre Doherty has had poems published in various literary journals. Her work was shortlisted for the Hennessy Poetry Award 2012 and The Bridport Prize 2012. She is working on a first collection that will focus on the psychological landscape.

Luna Dolezal is an Irish Research Council Postdoctoral Fellow in the Department of Philosophy, Trinity College Dublin. Her book, *The Body and Shame: Phenomenology, Feminism and the Socially Shaped Body*, will be published by Lexington Books in 2014.

Cheryl Donahue is a writer and website developer who began writing poems a few years ago, and has been published in *The Stinging Fly* and *WOW!*. She obtained a Masters in Interactive Media from University College Cork last year, and is trying to tell stories via new media with the skills acquired. She recently returned to the US after fifteen years in Ireland, and now lives in Philadelphia.

Michael J. Farrell lives in County Longford and writes short stories and novels. A story collection, *Life in the Universe*, was published by the Stinging Fly Press in 2009.

Diarmuid Fitzgerald was born in 1977, grew up in County Cork and went to college in NUI Maynooth. He lived in Japan for three years and now lives in Dublin, where he works as a schoolteacher. He has had haiku published in the anthology *100 Poets on Mount Ogura, One Poem Each* (Kyoto: Hailstone Publications, 2010).

Patrick FitzSymons has worked for years in TV and film on both sides of the camera. His screenplay 'A Year of Greater Love' aired on the BBC in 2012, the year in which he also completed an MA at the Seamus Heaney Centre at Queen's University Belfast. He and his family are again living in the city after a five-year sojourn on the north coast.

Deirdre Gleeson lives in Dublin. Two of her stories have previously been published by *The Stinging Fly*: one in the anthology, *Let's Be Alone Together* (2008), and the other in our Summer 2010 issue.

Kerry Hardie has published six collections of poetry, all with Gallery Press, the most recent of which is *The Ash and the Oak and the Wild Cherry Tree* (2012). She has also published two novels and is working on a third. Her *Selected Poems* was published by the Gallery Press (Ireland) and Bloodaxe (UK) in 2011.

John Kelly's most recent fiction appeared in the anthology *Silver Threads of Hope* edited by Sinead Gleeson (New Island, 2012). A novel entitled *From Out of The City* is due from Dalkey Archive Press in the autumn.

Diana Lueptow lives in Akron, Ohio. Her work has been published in *Arion, Beloit Poetry Journal, FIELD,* and elsewhere. She holds an MFA in poetry from Warren Wilson College in Asheville, North Carolina.

Noel Monahan has published five collections of poetry. His most recent publication was *Curve Of The Moon*, published by Salmon Poetry in 2010. He has won several national literary awards for his poetry and drama. His poetry was prescribed text for the Leaving Certificate English Course in 2011 and 2012. He is co-editor of Windows Publications and holds an MA in Creative Writing.

Sinéad Morrissey is the author of four collections of poetry from Carcanet Press. Her last three (*Between Here and There, The State of the Prisons* and *Through the Square Window*) were all shortlisted for the T.S. Eliot Prize. *Through the Square Window* won the Irish Times/Poetry Now Award in 2010.

Mary Noonan's poems have been published in print and online magazines in Ireland, Britain and the US, and at the audio-archive fishousepoems.org. She was awarded the Listowel Poetry Collection Prize in June 2010. Her first collection, *The Fado House*, was published by Dedalus Press in 2012.

Madeleine O'Callaghan was born and educated in Ireland. She now lives and works in Cambridge in the East of England. Her writing in prose and poetry has been published in England and the United States.

Paul Perry is a poet and fiction writer. His most recent book is *The Last Falcon and Small Ordinance* (The Dedalus Press, 2010). With Karen Gillece, he has written *The Innocent Sleep*, a 'Karen Perry' thriller to be published by Penguin (UK) and Henry Holt (USA) in 2014.

Pascale Petit's latest collection, *What the Water Gave Me: Poems after Frida Kahlo* (Seren, 2010), was shortlisted for both the TS Eliot prize and Wales Book of the Year, and was a Book of the Year in *The Observer*. She leads poetry courses at Tate Modern.

Nora Pyne lives in Dublin. 'Jeopardy' is her first story to be published.

C.K. Stead's novel, *Risk*, was launched by MacLehose Press in London last October and a new collection of poems, *The Yellow Buoy*, will be published by Auckland University Press this month to be followed later in the year by a UK edition from Arc. He lives in New Zealand.

Matthew Sweeney's latest collection, *Horse Music*, has just appeared from Bloodaxe (February 2013). A satirical thriller, set in the world of contemporary poetry, co-written with the English poet, John Hartley Williams, was published in November 2012 by the Muswell Press under the title *Death Comes for the Poets*.

Grace Wells was our featured poet in Issue 10 Volume Two, Summer 2008. Her debut collection, *When God Has Been Called Away to Greater Things* (Dedalus Press, 2010), won the Rupert and Eithne Strong Award and was shortlisted for the London Festival Fringe New Poetry Award.

Subscribe to The Stinging Fly

Three issues: €25 IRL & NI / €30 overseas

Six issues: €45 IRL & NI / €54 overseas

Pay online via paypal at www.stingingfly.org

Pay by bank transfer – instructions on our website

Send a cheque / postal order to:

The Stinging Fly, PO Box 6016, Dublin 1, Ireland

Keep in touch: sign up to our e-mail newsletter, become a fan on Facebook, or follow us on Twitter for regular updates about all our publications, events and activities.

www.stingingfly.org | www.facebook.com/StingingFly | @stingingfly